SENSORIMOTOR LEARNING

from Research
to Teaching

Virginia Lee Bell

California State College

Los Angeles

GOODYEAR PUBLISHING COMPANY, INC.

Pacific Palisades, California

Library of Congress Catalog Card Number: 71-104832

Current printing (last number):

10 9 8 7 6 5 4 3 2 1

Printed in the United States of America

To Ruth B. Glassow
PROFESSOR EMERITUS, UNIVERSITY OF WISCONSIN

Preface

For many years, motor learning as a subject area within physical education undergraduate curricula has been integrated into the total program, its various aspects being taught within other courses. During recent years, however, this area has been receiving individual emphasis, particularly at the graduate level. The need for such an emphasis on the undergraduate level has become apparent, resulting in the development of appropriate college courses. This book is intended to serve as a text for undergraduate students majoring in physical education, and material is presented which will be of value in the actual teaching and planning of activity programs.

A comprehensive review of the literature in motor learning would include a majority of studies related to verbal and fine motor skills, and motor tasks unlike those found in physical education. Although the experienced researcher would generalize to physical education with caution, such studies are less useful to the student; therefore, an attempt is made here to provide undergraduates with information from studies using motor tasks like those he will be teaching. Since generalizations from unlike studies have often provided the stimulus for related studies, such research is included to some extent, although the emphasis is on studies employing gross motor skills.

Sensorimotor Learning includes an introductory section dealing with basic research techniques and neurological concepts underlying sensory input, integration, and motor output. Successive chapters dealing with research are divided into two parts: sensory input and motor output. Discussions designed to stimulate thinking and further discussion about the best methods of applying knowledge gained in research to the actual teaching situation are followed by generalizations. Theories of learning are presented as they relate to specific areas of motor learning such as transfer, and the last part of the book presents ideas for program planning. Statistical understandings necessary for conducting classroom research are presented in an appendix.

Sincere appreciation is expressed to Miss Brenda Reilly for drawing the original sketches used for illustrations and to Miss Dava Reeder for typing the original manuscript. Appreciation is also expressed to colleagues for their advice and criticism and to students in undergraduate classes who, through their questions, pointed out the need for a book geared for the future teacher.

Contents

part one

BASIC UNDERSTANDING

Basic to the understanding of how motor learning takes place is a knowledge of the function of the nervous system. Learning is the process of integrating sensory information for motor output. The first chapter of this book deals with the gross anatomy of the nervous system and its function, and offers theoretical suggestions for consideration in planning the learning process. It is anticipated that in the near future theoretical suggestions such as those presented in this chapter will become the basis for experimental research related to the learning of motor skills.

The major portion of this book is devoted to a review and discussion of research related to the learning of gross motor skills. Chapter 2 explores concepts basic to the understandings required by the student in reading research as it is presented in this book and in its original form.

1

Neurological Basis of Motor Learning

During the heat of a closely fought game, the highly skilled basketball player shoots for the basket. The ball arches perfectly and swishes through the basket for two points. The performer has taken into account the events outside his body; knowledge of the distance of the basket has come to him through vision; he has heard the sound of an opponent approaching him; he feels the size, shape and texture of the ball. Knowledge of the internal world is also available. Joint receptors make known the position of the body parts. Muscle spindles and Golgi tendon organs signal impressions of the state of contraction of muscles. The cortical decision to shoot, the sensory information, and the kinesthetic memory of the learned movement are integrated within the nervous system. The result of this integration causes the muscular contraction necessary for the movement which in turn results in the perfect shot. How did this performer learn the motor skill? What events took place within his nervous system so that a given stimulus effected a skilled act?

THE LEARNING PROCESS

Knowledge of the internal processes involved in learning is far from complete. It is generally agreed that there are two phases in learning a motor skill. As the learner attempts a new movement he consciously motor plans many of its parts; he also perceives many sensory cues. The movement is awkward and full of unnecessary tension. During the second phase of learning the motor act becomes automatic. This takes place through repetition. Tension decreases and the neural direction of movement takes place at subconscious levels of function.

The role of the physical educator is to hasten the process of learning the motor act. Because a motor act is the result of integration of sensory input and repetition of the performance of the act, the physical education must be concerned with the types of sensory input which will hasten learning as well as the types of practice conditions which are most effective in the repetition of movement. The major portion of this book is devoted to presentation and discussion of the research which deals with uncovering the factors influencing the learning of motor skills found in physical education activities.

Inasmuch as the nervous system is responsible for directing motor acts and the process of learning skilled movements found in physical education activities, an understanding of the function of the nervous system is basic to an understanding of the learning process. This chapter is designed to acquaint the student of motor learning with the gross anatomy of the nervous system, its function, and specialized systems within the nervous system.

GROSS ANATOMY AND LEVELS OF FUNCTION

The main function of the central nervous system is the *integration* of sensory input for smooth motor output. The elements that are integrated include *volition,* or the will to do something; *sensations,* or knowledge of the internal and external world; and *inherent patterns* such as basic movement patterns including walking and reflexes. Information travels through the nervous system in the form of impulses conducted over nerve fibers; an impulse is a wave of excitation in response to a stimulus traveling along a nerve fiber. In order to understand how integration takes place it is necessary to have a knowledge of the gross anatomy of the nervous system and an understanding of how it functions. The five levels of function in descending order are the cerebral cortex, the basal ganglia, the cerebellum, the brain stem and the spinal cord.

the cerebral cortex

The brain has two cortical hemispheres which have convolutions called gyri and depressions called sulci. These gyri have been named and numbered and functions have been attributed to specific gyri. The sulci have also been named and more prominent sulci divide the cortex into lobes (see Figure 1.1). The central sulcus lies

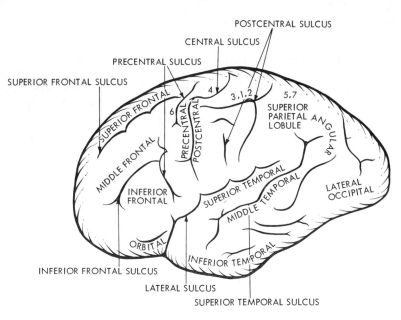

Figure 1.1   The Cerebral Cortex

between the frontal and parietal lobes. The lateral sulcus is between the temporal and frontal lobes and the occipital lobe is posterior to the parietal and temporal lobes. Anterior to the central sulcus is the pre-central sulcus. The gyrus between them, number 4, is concerned with fine motor activities. The area anterior to that, number 6, is concerned with gross motor activities. The parietal lobe of the cortex contains the post central gyrus, numbers 3, 1, and 2, and is concerned with sensation and perception. Areas 5, and 7 are concerned with sensory association. The temporal lobes are the receptive areas for hearing, and the occipital lobes for vision. The cortex is composed of gray matter which means that it is made up of the bodies of nerve cells.

Voluntary movements are initiated at the level of the cortex. For example one might decide to shoot for a basket or swim the crawl stroke. If the movements have not yet been learned the cortex "motor plans" what will take place. A beginning swimmer would consciously plan what his legs must do, think about bending his elbows at the right moment, and consider the placement of his hand in the water. Sensory stimuli are perceived, interpreted and associated at the level of the cortex. This implies a conscious awareness of sensory input.

basal ganglia

Deep to the cortex is white matter made up of the fibers of nerve cells and masses of gray matter called the basal ganglia. Although the thalamus and hypothalamus are included as basal ganglia, functionally they are related to the brain stem (see Figure 1.2).

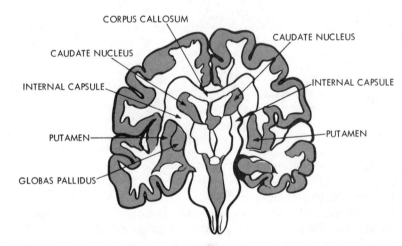

Figure 1.2   Basal Ganglia

Learned gross motor movements are initiated at the level of the basal ganglia. The swimmer having learned the front crawl may will to do that stroke at the cortical or conscious level but no longer needs to motor plan the movements. Thus, they are initiated at a lower unconscious level of function. Background posture is also initiated at this level. While reading this text you have assumed a posture unconsciously. The posture is the background for the conscious work of perceiving what you are reading. If you are taking notes, the cortex voluntarily decides what you will write and the basal ganglia initiate the movements necessary for the formation of the letters and the posture necessary to maintain a writing position.

the cerebellum

The cortex of the cerebellum is composed of gray matter and the interior of both white matter and gray matter. Like the cerebral cortex, the cerebellum has two hemispheres. These are attached to the brain stem by the cerebellar peduncles which carry nerve fibers.

Impulses from all receptors travel to the cerebellum. Impulses from the eyes, ears, proprioceptors, etc. are integrated. The results of integration of these impulses enable one to have coordinated movements and to judge time and distance. For example, in reaching out to pick up an object, appropriate muscles must contract to a certain degree and antagonistic muscles must relax. Visual impulses related to distance are integrated with proprioceptive impulses. Motor impulses to the muscles mediate the contraction of the movers and inhibition of the antagonists so that you can go directly to the object and grasp it without falling short of the target or over-reaching. The cerebellum is also concerned with integration of impulses related to posture and locomotion. Activity in the cerebellum is unconscious and the results of this activity play a part in the many feedback systems of the central nervous system.

the brain stem

The midbrain, pons, and medulla oblongata together are known as the brain stem. Masses of gray and white matter within the brain stem are known as the reticular formation. Cranial nerves arise from or terminate in nuclei in the brain stem. They include the trigeminal nerves V, the abducent nerves VI, the facial nerves VII, and the vestibulo-cochlear nerves VIII which are attached to the pons. Attached to the medulla oblongata are the glossopharyngeal nerves IX, the vagus nerves X, the accessory nerves XI, and the hypoglossal nerves XII. The oculomotor nerves III and the trochlear nerve IV arise from the midbrain (see Figure 1.3).

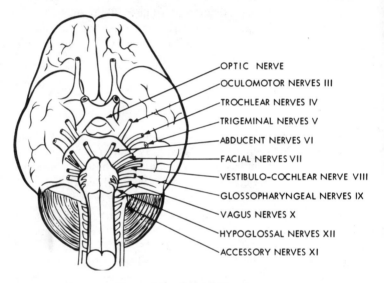

Figure 1.3   Cranial Nerves

The brain stem is important in integration of many impulses from the spinal cord, the cranial nerves, and the cerebellum. Sensory information concerned with joint position and movement is received from the medial lemniscal system. Information from the vestibular system regarding the sense of motion and the position of the head in space is received in the vestibular nuclei. The reticular formation and associated ascending reticular activating system which will be discussed in detail later are responsible for arousal of the cortex. Excitatory and inhibitory mechanisms control efferent impulses to the spinal cord and the muscles.

the spinal cord

The spinal cord is made up of gray and white matter. Figure 1.4 is a slice through the cord. The gray matter contains motor nerve

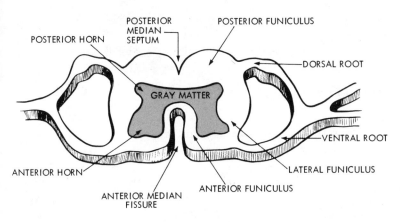

Figure 1.4   Spinal Cord

cells in the anterior horn and sensory nerve cells in the posterior horn. Tracts to and from higher levels of function make up the white matter. They are arranged in funiculi which are named in accordance with their location and include the anterior funiculus, the lateral funiculus and the posterior funiculus. Nerve fibers from the spinal nerves enter via the dorsal root. These are sensory or afferent fibers. Motor or efferent fibers to muscles leave the cord over the ventral root. The anterior median fissure lies between the anterior funiculi and the posterior median septum between the posterior funiculi.

The spinal cord carries the efferent and afferent fibers to and from the peripheral nerves. Higher level activity is integrated with spinal reflexes in the cord.

Spinal reflexes include the monosynaptic or stretch reflex. This is a two-neuron reflex and is exemplified by the familiar stretch reflex in the knee. As the tendon in the knee is tapped and the muscle is stretched, impulses travel to the cord over an afferent fiber. There is a direct synapse, a junction between nerve fibers, with the efferent fiber to the same muscle. The impulses to the muscle facilitate its contraction.

Another spinal reflex is the tonic lumbar reflex. Its name implies that it is a postural reflex and that the receptors are in the lumbar region of the spine. If the body is twisted backward to the right, the right arm and left leg are facilitated for flexion; the left arm and right leg for extension. As the body twists forward to the left, the right arm and left leg are facilitated for extension; the left arm and right leg for flexion. This is similar to the throwing pattern. In throwing, however, the left knee is usually flexed on the follow through. Thus we have an example of a reflex pattern which must be overcome for the development of a skilled movement.

ASCENDING PATHWAYS

Impulses related to sensations ascend the spinal cord to the thalamus over afferent, or sensory, pathways which fall into categories. The names of the categories tell where they are located. Spinothalamic pathways travel from the spine to the thalamus carrying information related to survival and protection. This information alerts the cortex that something is wrong somewhere but does not discriminate in terms of where it is wrong. For example if a person burns himself, pain information would reach the cortex via a spinothalamic pathway, arousing the cortex but not mediating the perception of where the burn is spatially.

There are two spinothalamic tracts named for the funiculi in which they lie. The anterior spinothalamic tract receives touch impulses over the dorsal root of the spinal cord. There is a synapse and information crosses to the tract in the anterior funiculus on the opposite side of the cord which ascends to the level of the thalamus. While traveling through the brain stem the anterior spinothalamic tracts join a tract called the medial lemniscus which ends at the thalamus. Impulses from the thalamus are relayed to the parietal lobe of the cortex.

Information related to pain and temperature enters the cord over the dorsal root where there is a synapse. Impulses then cross to the opposite lateral funiculus where they ascend in the lateral funiculus to the thalamus. This is called the lateral spinothalamic tract.

The posterior column medial lemniscal tracts form a discriminative or spatial information system. Again the name tells that the tracts ascend in the posterior funiculus to the medial lemniscus which terminates in the thalamus. Information related to light touch, pressure and kinesthesis enters the cord over afferent fibers in the dorsal root. It ascends to the medulla oblongata on the same side, synapses, crosses and ascends to the thalamus in the opposite medial lemniscus. This information is also relayed to the parietal lobe of the cortex.

Impulses from the skin and proprioceptors, which are found in muscles, tendons, and joints, ascend to the cerebellum via anterior and posterior cerebellar tracts on the same side of the cord. Impulses from cranial nerves and brain stem nuclei are also relayed to the cerebellum.

DESCENDING PATHWAYS

Efferent, or motor, pathways descend in the central nervous system and fall into two major categories. The pyramidal system, so named because the fibers pass through the pyramids on the medulla oblongata, is a direct path from the cortex to the spinal cord. Specific tracts are appropriately named cortico-spinal. The extrapyramidal system includes all other descending tracts, none of which pass through the pyramids.

the pyramidal system

Cortico-spinal fibers arise in the area of the precentral gyrus and descend to the medulla oblongata. At this level 70 percent of the fibers cross and descend in the lateral funiculus of the spinal cord. At the level of the spinal cord another 15 percent of the cortico-spinal fibers cross and also descend in the lateral funiculus. These are named lateral cortico-spinal tracts. The 15 percent of the cortico-spinal fibers that remain descend on the same side in the anterior and lateral funiculi. In the cord the fibers synapse with internuncial neurons which in turn synapse with the motor efferent fibers to muscles. Because there are so few synapses, the pyramidal system is not as involved in sensory motor integration as the extrapyramidal system.

the extrapyramidal system

There are many tracts to the brain stem from the cortex, basal ganglia, cerebellum, and cranial nerves. Impulses from these tracts reach excitatory or inhibitory mechanisms in the brain stem. Resulting control over gross motor activity is mediated via impulses traveling over the extrapyramidal system.

The vestibulo-spinal and reticulo-spinal tracts which come from the excitatory mechanisms descend in the anterior funiculus. The reticulo-spinal tract which descends in the lateral funiculus carries impulses from inhibitory mechanisms. At the level of the cord there are synapses with internuncial neurons which in turn synapse with motor efferents to muscles.

servomechanisms

There are many connections between the structures of the central nervous system which form circuits or servomechanisms over which internal feedback is mediated following integration. The gamma system, which will be discussed in detail, is an example of a servomechanism. The cerebellum is involved in a servomechanism for error control of movements. Impulses from the muscles reach the cerebellum, where they are evaluated, integrated, and projected to other nuclei in the brain, and then descend to correct muscle activity. Servomechanisms mediate the integration of sensory input which is necessary for motor output.

SPECIAL SYSTEMS

There are a number of systems in the nervous system which have special functions. Three of these are of particular interest to the student of motor learning and will be discussed in detail. They include the vestibular system, the ascending reticular activating system, and feedback systems related to proprioception.

the vestibular system

The vestibular system is a system which should be of great interest to the physical educator inasmuch as it is involved with kinesthesis, balance, and postural reflexes. This system is related to the sense of motion and the position of the head in space.

The vestibular system is related to the inner ear, the vestibular nerve and the vestibular nuclei. Structurally the inner ear includes a labyrinth composed of three parts. They are the semicircular canals, the vestibule and the cochlea. The semicircular canals and the vestibule are part of the vestibular system, whereas the cochlea is concerned with hearing (see Figure 1.5).

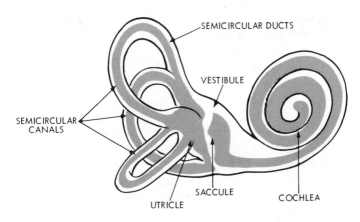

Figure 1.5 Vestibular System

There are semicircular ducts, filled with fluid, in the semi-circular canals. In the ducts are hairs whose cells are imbedded in gelatin. Vestibular nerve fibers terminate at the base of the hair cells. When the pressure of the fluid in the ducts changes the nerves are activated. Pressure changes are caused by inertia: for example, if the head is turned to the right, the fluid tends to remain stationary. Therefore this part of the vestibular system is geared for information about acceleration and deceleration of movement.

The vestibule is a chamber containing two sacs called the utricle and saccule. Hairs project into the sacs, and the vestibular nerve terminates around the cells of the hairs. Small calcium masses called otoliths deflect the hairs when the position of the head changes. Therefore this part of the vestibular system receives information related to the head in space.

The vestibular portion of the acoustic nerve relays information to the vestibular nuclei located in the brain stem and to the cerebellum. Descending tracts from the vestibular nuclei are called vestibulo-spinal tracts. They carry impulses to the cord which ultimately affect muscular contraction. Fibers from the vestibular nuclei also reach the nuclei of the oculomotor nerve. Thus there is a direct relationship between head movements and eye movements.

The vestibular system plays an important role in integration, particularly in the brain stem and the cerebellum. Thus, if the physical educator wishes to stimulate integration within the central nervous system he might select activities related to balance, tumbling, diving, or starting and stopping. Actually, it can be theorized that all activities would stimulate the vestibular system; however, those just mentioned are possibly the more basic activities.

The tonic labyrinthine reflexes influence efferent impulses to the postural muscles. If the head is prone, all four limbs are facilitated for increased flexor tone. Conversely when the head is supine all four limbs are facilitated for increased extensor tone. With the head to the side the extremities on the side with the ear down are facilitated for increased extensor tone and the other extremities for increased flexor tone. It can be seen that in many activities, head position can play an important role as an aid to the activity, whereas in other activities the reflex must be overcome. For example in the handstand the head is prone in relation to the pull of gravity; the tonic labyrinthine reflex would facilitate flexor tone. The performer, however, must maintain an extended position. In the forward roll, tucking the head would aid in facilitating the flexor tone necessary for the correct body position.

the ascending reticular activating system

The reticular formation, which is located in the brain stem, receives collaterals from the spino-thalamic tracts and afferent fibers from nuclei in the brain stem. Thus many sensory impulses go into the reticular formation. The reticular formation has fibers to the thalamus over which impulses ascend. Impulses are then projected from the thalamus to the cortex. The impulses which reach the cortex arouse it so that sensations arriving over direct pathways can be perceived. The reticular formation receives impulses from the cortex; thus, the cortex can modify the activity of the reticular formation. It can be set so that it allows only certain kinds of information to reach the cortex. This is the neurological reason for using motivating devices in teaching. If the student wants to attend to what is going on, the cortex will be activated by the reticular activating system; this is necessary for perception and learning. An example of setting the reticular formation for learning occurs when you study with the radio on. If you want to attend to whatever you are studying, the sounds are filtered out so that you may concentrate. Thus the reticular formation can receive and reject sensory information.

proprioception

Proprioceptors are receptors related to kinesthetic sensations. They include the muscle spindle, the Golgi tendon organ and the Ruffini endings found in joint capsules. The term kinesthetic sensation implies that these receptors send sensory impulses to the central nervous system where they are integrated with impulses from other receptors for motor output. This does not imply that these impulses reach the level of the cortex.

The muscle spindle. The muscle spindle is an unusual receptor. As in all receptors, afferent fibers carry sensory impulses to the central nervous system. In addition there are, in the muscle spindle, contractile fibers which receive motor impulses over efferent fibers. The muscle fibers which contract to move body parts or maintain posture are called extrafusal fibers, whereas the fibers inside the muscle spindle are known as intrafusal fibers. Muscle spindles are parallel with the extrafusal fibers and may bridge the space from tendon to tendon (Figure 1.6), or lie in tandem from tendon to tendon (Figure

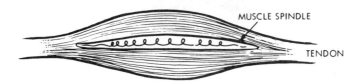

Figure 1.6   Muscle Spindle in Extrafusal Fibers

1.7). Within the spindle there are two types of intrafusal fibers known as nuclear bag fibers and nuclear chain fibers. Sensory endings terminate around the intrafusal fibers. There are two kinds of sensory afferents: the primary (annulospiral), which is fast conducting and has endings on both the nuclear bag and the nuclear chain, and the secondary (flower spray), which is slower conducting and has endings on the nuclear chain (Figure 1.8). Motor efferents to the muscle spindle are called gamma fibers. Gamma 1 (also called phasic gamma, dynamic gamma, or gamma plate) fibers have endings on Gamma 2 (also called static gamma, tonic gamma or gamma trail) fibers have endings on the nuclear chain (Figure 1.9). Alpha fibers

Figure 1.7   Muscle Spindles in Tandem

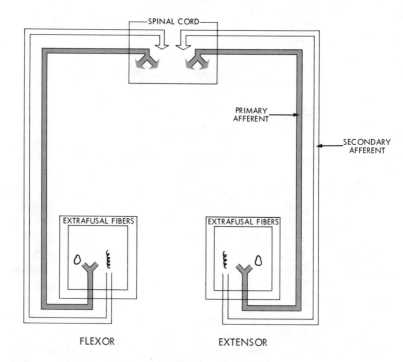

Figure 1.8   Schema Afferents

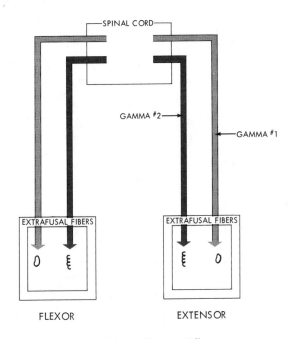

Figure 1.9 Schema Gamma Efferents

are efferent or motor fibers from the spinal cord to the extrafusal muscle fibers (Figure 1.10). They are functionally related to the afferent fibers of the entire system, which is known as the gamma system or gamma loop (Figure 1.11).

The afferent fibers carry impulses related to changes in length of the spindle and the velocity of these changes. The primary afferent and nuclear bag are associated with changes in velocity. The nuclear chain and the primary and secondary endings which terminate on it are associated with static changes in length. The afferents may be activated in two ways. As a muscle is stretched by some external force such as the contraction of its antagonist, the spindles within the muscle are lengthened, causing the appropriate afferents to carry sensory information to the spinal cord. When the gamma efferents carry motor impulses to the intrafusal fibers causing them to contract, the nuclear region of the fibers is lengthened and again the appropriate afferents carry impulses to the spinal cord. Figure 1.12 is a schematic diagram showing how contraction can cause lengthening.

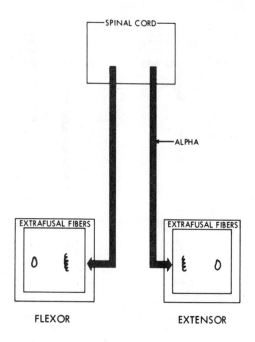

Figure 1.10   Schema Alpha Fibers

The springs represent the contractile portion of the intrafusal fibers; if they contract, the material in the central portion, which represents the nuclear region of the intrafusal fibers, is lengthened. By sending impulses over the gamma efferents the central nervous system can keep the spindle taut, thus activating the afferents. This is called *setting the spindle*. Unless the spindle is set by impulses from the gamma efferents, the spindle would shorten as the extrafusal fibers contract and the afferents would cease firing. This is called *unloading the spindle*.

The primary afferent responds to phasic or dynamic lengthening. Thus it may be activated by stretch of the extrafusal fibers of the muscle or by impulses reaching the nuclear bag via gamma 1. It in turn activates the alpha fiber to the extrafusal fibers of the muscle in which it lies and facilitates phasic contraction of that muscle. Antagonists are inhibited. The secondary afferent responds to static or tonic lengthening. It can be activated by stretch or by impulses to the nuclear chain via gamma 2. In turn, impulses from the secondary

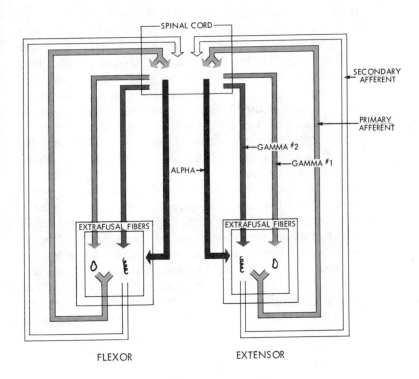

SPINAL CORD

SECONDARY AFFERENT

PRIMARY AFFERENT

GAMMA #2

GAMMA #1

ALPHA

EXTRAFUSAL FIBERS

EXTRAFUSAL FIBERS

FLEXOR

EXTENSOR

Figure 1.11 Schema Gamma System

afferent reach the alpha fibers and cause facilitation of flexors for tonic contraction and inhibition of extensors. Impulses from the nuclear chain which travel over the primary afferent to the alpha fibers of flexors can facilitate the tonic contraction of flexors.

Again looking at Figure 1.11, we can trace what takes place within the gamma loop. If one wills voluntarily to pick up an object from the table, information from receptors such as the eyes and the muscle spindle is integrated in the brain. Motor impulses then travel over the descending tracts to gamma 1 of the appropriate muscle spindles, setting the spindle so that it remains taut until the object has

Figure 1.12 Schema Muscle Spindle

been reached. Nuclear bag fibers contract, thus activating the primary afferent which conducts sensory impulses to the spinal cord. Alpha fibers to that same muscle then carry impulses facilitating its contraction until the object has been reached. At this point impulses to the spindle diminish, thus unloading the spindle. In many movements dynamic contraction of one muscle is preceded by the dynamic contraction of its antagonist. This places the muscle on stretch and lengthens the nuclear bag, causing the primary afferent to fire. Impulses then travel over the alpha to the muscle which has been stretched, facilitating dynamic contraction. The antagonist is inhibited and synergists are facilitated.

In the tonic contraction necessary for maintenance of posture, alternating contractions are taking place on both sides of a joint. To trace what happens within the gamma loop it is necessary to consider flexors and extensors separately. If an extensor is stretched by contraction of its antagonist, or if the nuclear chain fibers within an extensor contract as the result of impulses reaching it via gamma 2, the secondary afferent will relay impulses to the cord. The extensor will then be inhibited via information traveling over the alpha fiber. The flexor will be facilitated via impulses traveling over its alpha fiber. If the environmental demand is that an extensor contract tonically, impulses will travel over the primary afferent to the cord. Motor impulses facilitating contraction will then reach the muscle via the alpha fiber. If a flexor is stretched as in postural sway, or the nuclear chain is activated by gamma 2, impulses will travel to the cord over the secondary afferent. Motor impulses to the extrafusal fibers will travel over the alpha fiber to the flexor, facilitating tonic contraction.

In structuring the learning situation, the physical educator can take advantage of knowledge related to the gamma system. By instructing students to take a backswing before a forward movement, the instructor ensures that the muscles involved in the forward movement will be dynamically stretched. Impulses will travel over the primary afferents and the alphas to those muscles, facilitating their contraction on the forward swing. When static contraction of flexors is required, students should be instructed to place body parts in a position which stretches extensors, since the extensors will be inhibited and the flexors facilitated. If it is desirable to place a muscle on stretch, a rapid movement would dynamically lengthen the spindle, facilitating the contraction of that muscle. Slow stretch, therefore, is more desirable than rapid bouncing movements.

The Golgi tendon organ. This proprioceptor is found in the tendons of muscles as its name implies. Nerve fibers supply one or more Golgi tendon organs, which respond to tension in the tendon. Tension can exist due to stretch and muscle contraction. Impulses from the Golgi tendon organ are relayed to the cerebellum where they cause inhibition of the muscle in which they lie and facilitation of the antagonistic muscle. Thus, like the muscle spindle, this proprioceptor does not play a part in conscious perception of movement.

Ruffini endings. Ruffini endings are proprioceptive nerve endings found in joint capsules, where they record joint position and movement. The exact functional relation of these receptors to motor output is not yet known; however, it is generally agreed that conscious perception of movement is due to information from the Ruffini endings being relayed to the cortex via the medial lemniscal system.

DISCUSSION

Research related to the nervous system has primarily been conducted by neurologists. Its purpose has been to determine how the structures in the nervous system function and relate. Generally the subjects used in such research are animals and findings are generalized to the functioning of man's nervous system. The implications of this knowledge are usually theoretical and are derived by psychologists, therapists, and educators who strive to make applications in practical situations. Further research should be conducted by physical educators to test the validity of applications in the learning situation.

Neurologists have suggested that there are two phases in learning and that repetition of a motor task is necessary to reach the second phase in which the task becomes automatic. This implies the need for practice. The major portion of this book is devoted to research related to various types of practice of motor tasks. Little research has been done, however, on the amount of repetition necessary to reach the automatic phase of performing a motor task.

Since sensory input is integrated for motor output, the physical educator should pay attention to the sensory information available to the learner. Considerable research has been conducted related to forms of communicating to the learner and to methods of supplying him with knowledge of results, both of which are sensory input. Little is known about the types of sensory information which will aid the learner during the actual performance of a movement. The learner has much information available to him through vision, hearing, touch, and kinesthesis. The importance and relationship of this information is a subject for further study.

The importance of motivation has a neurological foundation. The cortex of a motivated learner will set the reticular formation so that more information is perceived. Methods of motivating students in physical education classes are chosen based on the judgment of the teacher. Although further study is indicated, motivation is a difficult subject for study because the use of motivating devices will interact with the self-motivation of the learner and because different people are motivated by different stimuli.

Knowledge of reflexes is probably the most unused source of neurological information as it relates to the learning of motor skills. The position of body parts prior to or during the performance of a movement may have a profound effect upon the ability to perform the task. The physical educator should strive to devise teaching cues which will assist the performer in making effective use of reflex actions.

GENERALIZATIONS

1. Repetition of a motor task is necessary for performance of the task to become automatic.

2. Integration of sensory information is necessary for smooth motor output.

3. Balance activities may facilitate integration within the central nervous system through the vestibular system.

4. Motivating the learner is important for his perception of sensory information.

5. A knowledge of reflexes will enable the teacher to provide cues which will aid the learner in using or overcoming reflex actions.

BIBLIOGRAPHY

Adrian, Lord E. D. 1959. Sensory mechanisms. *Neurophysiology: handbook of physiology* 1:1:365–68. Washington, D.C.: American Physiological Society.

Barker, David, ed. 1962. *Symposium on muscle receptors*. Hong Kong: Hong Kong University Press.

Boyd, Ian, et al. 1968. *The role of the gamma system in movement and posture*. New York: Association for the Aid of Crippled Children.

Burr, Harold Sexton. 1960. *The neural basis of human behavior*. Springfield, Illinois: Charles C Thomas.

Denny-Brown, Derek. 1960. Motor mechanisms. *Neurophysiology: handbook of physiology* 2:1:781–96. Washington, D.C.: American Physiological Society.

Eccles, John Carew. 1953. *The neurophysiological basis of mind*. Oxford: Clarendon Press.

Eldred, Earl. 1960. Posture and locomotion. *Neurophysiology: handbook of physiology* 2:1:1067–88. Washington, D.C.: American Physiological Society.

French, J. D. 1957. The reticular formation. *Sci. Am.* 196:54.

———. 1960. The reticular formation. *Neurophysiology: handbook of physiology* 2:1:1281. Washington, D.C.: American Physiological Society.

Galambos, Robert, and Morgan, Clifford T. 1960. The neural basis of learning. *Neurophysiology: handbook of physiology* 3:1:1471–1500. Washington, D.C.: American Physiological Society.

Gardner, Ernest. 1963. *Fundamentals of neurology*. Philadelphia: W. B. Saunders Company.

Gernandt, B. E. 1959. Vestibular mechanisms. *Neurophysiology: handbook of physiology* 1:1:549. Washington, D.C.: American Physiological Society.

Granit, Ragnar. 1955. *Receptors and sensory perception*. New Haven: Yale University Press.

Hellebrant, Frances. 1958. Physiology of motor learning. *Cerebral Palsy Review* 19:4:9.

Henatsch, H. D., Manni, E.; and Dow, R. S. 1964. Effects of gamma loop interruption on cerebellar control of individual alpha motorneuron stretch reflexes. *J. Neurophys.* 28:193–209.

Henatsch, H. D.; Manni, E.; Wilson, J. H.; and Dow, R. S. 1964. Linked and independent responses of tonic alpha and gamma hindlimb motorneurons to deep cerebellar stimulation. *J. Neurophys.* 28:172–92.

Jung, Richard, and Hassler, Rolf. 1960. The extrapyramidal motor system. *Neurophysiology: handbook of physiology* 2:1:863–928. Washington, D.C.: American Physiological Society.

Livingston, Robert B. 1959. Central control of receptors and sensory transmission systems. *Neurophysiology: handbook of physiology* 1:1:741–60. Washington, D.C.: American Physiological Society.

Matthews, P. B. C. 1964. Muscle spindles and their motor control. *Physiol. Rev.* 44:219–88.

Neff, William D. 1960. Sensory discrimination. *Neurophysiology: handbook of physiology* 3:1:1447–70. Washington, D.C.: American Physiological Society.

Paillard, Jacques. 1960. The patterning of skilled movements. *Neurophysiology: handbook of physiology* 3:1:1679–1708. Washington, D.C.: American Physiological Society.

Penfield, Wilder. 1960. Neurophysiological basis of the higher functions of the nervous system. *Neurophysiology: handbook of physiology* 3:1:1441–46. Washington, D.C.: American Physiological Society.

Renkin, Barbara, and Vallbo, Ake B. 1964. Simultaneous responses of groups I and II cat muscle spindle afferents to muscle position and movement. *J. Neurophys.* 23:429–50.

Rose, Jerry E., and Mountcastle, Vernon B. 1959. Touch and kinestheses. *Neurophysiology: handbook of physiology* 1:1:387–415. Washington, D.C.: American Physiological Society.

Shambes, Georgia. 1968. Influence of the muscle spindle on posture and movement. *Phys. Ther. Rev.* 48:1094.

Terzulo, C. A., and Adly, W. R. 1960. Sensorimotor cortical activities. *Neurophysiology: handbook of physiology.* 2:1:797–836. Washington, D.C.: American Physiological Society.

2

Understanding Experimental Research

It is necessary to conduct experiments in order to determine how people learn to perform motor skills. In experimental research a trial is made and the results are observed and interpreted. For example, an investigator might have two groups of subjects try two different methods of practicing the same skill and observe the effects of these methods on the final performance of that skill. The data would then be interpreted to determine whether one method of practice was superior to the other method.

The first step in experimental research is the recognition of a problem. A problem is, in a sense, a mystery without a solution. In the area of motor learning, problems are related to finding those factors which yield the highest levels of performance. Some of the factors that have been studied are methods of communicating to the learner, procedures of supplying knowledge of results, and various methods of practicing skills.

Following the recognition of the problem, the investigator should limit the problem to a specific age, skill level, sex, population, and motor skill or skills. A study is then designed to find the solution to the problem.

RESEARCH DESIGN

The investigator should decide whether to conduct the experiment in the laboratory or in the classroom. An understanding of the concepts of internal and external validity (Campbell and Stanley, 1963) will influence this decision. Control of *internal validity* means that for all subjects, all factors or *variables* should be the same except the *treatment variables* which are the factors or conditions under study. In the laboratory, the investigator has greater control over factors which might influence his results than he has in the classroom. In the classroom situation the investigator uses students assigned to the class as subjects, whereas in laboratory research a more unbiased method of selecting subjects can be employed. In addition, classroom influences such as interaction between students can be eliminated from the laboratory situation if subjects report one at a time. In the laboratory, environmental conditions are more easily controlled than in the classroom. Such controls give a study greater *internal validity,* and the results of the study are apt to reflect the effects of the treatment variables rather than the effects of uncontrolled variables.

The purpose of an investigation in motor learning is to generalize to the classroom. The more the investigation is like the classroom situation, the more basis one has for generalizations. *External validity* is the term used to describe this aspect of research design. Thus, although the internal validity of the research is more difficult to control in the classroom than in the laboratory, the external validity is greater in classroom research.

Regardless of whether the research is conducted in the laboratory or in the classroom, the investigator should attempt to make all conditions under which experimentation takes place consistent.

The application of the treatment variable should be consistent for all subjects. The treatment variable is usually a variable which is added to or subtracted from a situation. The effects of this process supply the facts which lead to the solution of the problem. For example, in an experiment to study the effects of a certain variable such as a teaching emphasis upon the learning of a motor skill, the number of times the variable is introduced and the way in which it is emphasized should be the same for each subject in that part of the experiment. All conditions under which experimentation takes place should be consistent.

Equipment is often utilized in experimentation involving motor performance. The equipment should provide all subjects with the opportunity to make the same response. For example, in an experiment in which balls are used, the condition of the ball can affect performance. It is generally best to use new balls. The surface which a ball meets should be the same throughout an experiment because balls rebound more quickly from one substance than another. In some experiments the time of day, or light conditions, may affect performance. The conditions which must be controlled should be determined in accordance with the nature of the problem.

The selection of the subjects should be carefully considered in designing research. Sex, age, skill level, and previous experience are factors which are identified in the selection of subjects. Most studies in motor learning use beginners as subjects because it is easier to ascertain that the subjects are equal in relation to these factors. Thus the internal validity of the study is increased.

The selection of subjects also has a bearing on the external validity of a study. Results of the study should only be generalized to groups of students like those used in the study. For example, if college students are used as subjects, results of the study should only be generalized to college students. Once the population from which the subjects will be drawn has been identified, the actual selection of individuals takes place. They may be selected *randomly*. For example, an investigator may decide to use male seventh graders from Lincoln Junior High School as subjects. All students fitting this description constitute the *population*. If there are 500 boys in the seventh grade and the investigator needs thirty boys for the experiment, he may select a random sample of that population. This means that each boy in the population is given a number from 1 to 500. Tables of random numbers developed by statisticians are used to select the thirty boys. For example, in reading a column in the table, the first number might be 425. The boy with that number will become a subject for the study. This procedure is followed until thirty boys have been selected. In contrast to a random sample, the investigator may decide to use *matched groups*. If the thirty boys are to be placed into two matched groups on the basis of scores on a skill test, each group will contain a boy with the same score. The groups, therefore, are *equated* on that basis.

In motor learning, the effects of the treatment variables upon performance in some skill are studied. The measure of performance is called the *dependent variable;* that is, it depends upon the effects of the treatment variable. Treatment or *independent variables* are manipulated by the investigator. These are the factors under study. If the investigator wishes to determine whether moving pictures or live demonstrations are better ways of communicating to the learner, these are the treatment variables. Performance in the skill after viewing the films or demonstrations is the dependent variable. A minimum of two *experimental groups* of subjects is necessary, each one receiving one of the treatment variables. The performance of a *control group* on the dependent variable might also be compared with the performance of the experimental groups. The control group does not receive a treatment variable. In the preceding example the control group would practice without viewing films or demonstrations.

The data or scores from the measurement of performance on the dependent variable must be statistically analyzed using an appropriate method. The investigator usually determines whether a group improves in performance or whether performance differs among groups. The word *significant* is used when this occurs. This is a statistical term which means that improvement or differences are meaningful and important and are not just due to chance. If there are two groups which show a significant difference in performance, the treatment variable used with the group having the higher scores is considered to be better than the other treatment variable. If there is no significant difference, then the effects of both treatment variables are the same and both may be used with equal effectiveness. These results of an investigation are called *findings.*

In a research report most investigators present a discussion. This is generally the most interesting part of the report. The implications for the use of the findings are presented. The findings are compared with those from related studies. The investigator may discuss observations he made during the study and attempt to explain why certain events took place. In addition, suggestions for further research may be presented or implied.

The final step in conducting research is to reach a *conclusion.* A conclusion is a generalized statement based on the findings. The conclusion may be applied in the teaching of students under conditions like those in the experiment.

MOTOR LEARNING INSTRUMENTATION

Although the purpose of this book is to present knowledge and understandings derived from research that is directly related to the teaching
of physical education, contributions from other disciplines are also of
importance. The instruments used by investigators have a direct
bearing upon the validity of a study. Many motor learning studies
have been completed by psychologists and engineers. Generally the
skills used are unlike those found in physical education, which limits
the extent to which the physical educators can generalize their conclusions to the classroom. These studies, however, have often stimulated
investigations by physical educators. Sometimes the findings from
studies using tasks unlike those found in physical education activities
and the findings from studies using physical education activities are in
agreement. In other cases, the nature of the task appears to have a
direct bearing upon the results. This is called an interaction. For
example, a finding may hold true for one type of task while a different
task performed under the same or similar conditions results in a contradictory finding.

In order to read, understand, and apply the related research,
it is necessary to have an understanding of the types of tasks and instruments used in investigations. Although the tasks used by investigators are innumerable, there are several tasks, in addition to physical
education skills, which have been used repeatedly. An understanding
of these tasks and the instrumentation involved is necessary in reading
the research and in realizing the comparative complexity of the types
of movements found in physical education.

line drawing

Many investigators have used line drawing as a motor skill.
Generally the subject is blindfolded and instructed to draw lines three
inches long. This task has often been used in studies related to knowledge of results. In some studies the subject is informed whether the
line he has drawn is right or wrong, in others he is told whether it is

too short or too long, and in some studies he is told the extent of his error in inches. On the basis of this information, the subject adjusts his movement and again attempts to draw lines three inches long.

With a partner as the "investigator," close your eyes and draw ten lines, attempting to make them three inches long. Have your partner measure each line with a ruler or three-by-five card and tell you whether each line was right or wrong. Compare the difficulty of making movement adjustments with those you might have to make if you missed the basket in shooting from the free throw line.

mirror tracing

A number of studies have employed mirror tracing. A star or some other pattern is placed on the table before the subject in such a way that it can only be seen in a mirror reflection (see Figure 2.1).

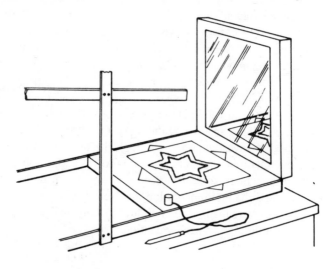

Figure 2.1   Mirror Tracing

Represented photographically in M. Dorothy Massey, "The Significance of Interpolated Time Intervals of Motor Learning," *Research Quarterly* 30(Oct. 1959):189

The subject is instructed to trace the star or other pattern and performance is measured in terms of time and errors.

Draw a star pattern on a piece of paper and then place it before a mirror. Have a partner hold a piece of paper above your hand so that you cannot see the star unless you look in the mirror. Attempt to trace your drawing. It is surprising how confusing this task can be, yet it can be learned.

stylus maze

A small stylus maze has often been used by psychologists. The maze in Figure 2.2 is a large maze designed by physical educators to

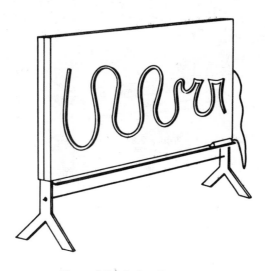

Figure 2.2 Stylus Maze

Represented photographically in B. J. Purdy, "Effect of Number of Practice Trials in Initial Learning on Retention and Relearning of Motor Skills" (Ph.D. diss., University of Southern California, 1964)

invoke large movements similar to those found in physical education. The edges of the maze are covered with copper which has been wired. The stylus which is held in the hand is also wired. The objective is to travel the maze with the stylus as quickly as possible without touching the copper. Each touch completes the electrical circuit and records an error on a counter. Performance is measured in terms of time and errors.

Draw a maze on the blackboard. With a piece of chalk, travel the maze as quickly as possible, trying not to touch the lines of the maze. Note how many times your chalk line touches the maze lines.

tracking tasks

There are many kinds of tracking tasks in which the subject must track or focus upon a moving target. The most common tracking task involves the pursuit rotor (see Figure 2.3). A round disk with a

Figure 2.3   Pursuit Rotor

small metal target revolves. The target is wired as is the stylus which the subject holds in his hand. The objective is to keep the stylus in contact with the target. When contact is maintained, a circuit is completed and the time on target is recorded on an electrical clock.

Place a round piece of paper on a record with a circle the size of a dime drawn near the edge for a target. Place the record on a record player at 78 rpm. Using a pencil as a stylus, attempt to maintain light contact with the target for a period of thirty seconds. Note how often the pencil marks are off target. Compare the arm movements with movements found in physical education activities.

stabilometer

There are several different types of stabilometers which have been designed to study balance. In general, a stabilometer consists of a platform on a fulcrum (see Figure 2.4). The subject stands on the platform and attempts to balance it. A clock is wired to the stabilometer in such a way that it stops when the platform touches the ground. In this way the time actually spent in balance is recorded.

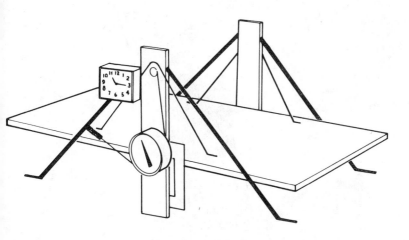

Figure 2.4 Stabilometer

Represented photographically in John C. Bachman, "Specificity vs. Generality in Learning and Performing Two Large Muscle Motor Tasks," *Research Quarterly* 32 (Mar. 1961): 3

bachman ladder climb

Bachman (1961) devised a balance activity employing a ladder which has been used in several studies (see Figure 2.5). The ladder is adjusted according to the vertical reach of the subject. The subject receives thirty-second trials during which he climbs as high as possible before losing balance. The rungs are numbered, and the highest rung reached constitutes the score. Scores for each climb made during the thirty seconds are added.

novel tasks

Some investigators choose to measure performance on novel tasks. These tasks involve movements which represent skills found in physical education activities but which are new to the subjects. An example might consist of bouncing a basketball into a target at a specific distance. A novel task affords greater internal validity in an investigation because the investigator knows that it has not been

Figure 2.5   Bachman Ladder Climb

From John C. Bachman, "Specificity vs. Generality in Learning and Performing Two Large Muscle Motor Tasks," *Research Quarterly* 32 (Mar. 1961): 3. Reprinted by permission.

practiced before, and it is not likely to be practiced outside of the investigation.

Devise a novel task involving a projectile and practice it twenty times daily for ten days. Keep a record of your performance and a daily diary in which you record any observations you make, such as the things you did to improve and any feelings you might have regarding your progress. Note how much improvement you made and keep this in mind as you read about the duration of motor learning investigations. Your observations will remind you of some of the frustrations of being a beginner and point out the need for the research which is being done in motor learning to hasten the acquisition of skill.

actual skills

Some investigators choose to use actual skills found in physical education activities. Such studies have greater external validity. In this situation, internal validity is controlled by ascertaining that subjects in the experimental and control groups begin practice at the same level of skill. With actual skills it is often possible to conduct an experiment without the subjects knowing they are in an experiment. This too increases external validity.

BIBLIOGRAPHY

Bachman, John C. 1961. Specificity vs. generality in learning and performing two large muscle motor tasks. *Research Quarterly* 32:3.

Campbell, D. T., and Stanley, J. C. 1963. Experimental and quasi-experimental designs for research on teaching. In *Handbook of Research on Teaching,* ed. N. L. Gage, pp. 171–246. American Educational Research Association.

part two
SENSORY INPUT

All forms of sensory input are integrated within the nervous system for motor output; there are two major forms of sensory input over which the physical educator has control. The first of these is the way in which he communicates to the learner. Research related to communication is presented in Chapter 3. The second form of sensory input follows performance and is called feedback or knowledge of results. Chapter 4 deals with research related to knowledge of results.

3

Communication

One of the roles of the teacher in physical education is to communicate to the learner. We must communicate in terms of the purpose of a skill, the form of a skilled movement, knowledge of rules, and understanding of strategy. Most research is related to the effects of various forms of communication upon the performance of skilled movements. Research related to communication generally consists of a study of the effect of adding a form of communication to a conventional teaching method, or a comparison of two or more methods of communicating. Once directed by the form of communication, the subjects practice the motor skill. Following practice, performance is measured. Differences between groups are analyzed, with the findings providing the means by which the treatment variables are evaluated. Investigations fall into four major categories: demonstration, manual assistance, verbal instruction, and a comparison of methods of communication.

Demonstration involves showing the learner the form of the movement through the use of live performance, motion pictures, loop films, pictures, filmstrips, and television. *Manual assistance* refers to guiding the learner physically as he performs a motor skill. *Verbal instruction* refers to methods of communication through oral explanation. Telling the learner what is expected of him, detailed explanation of a motor skill, concepts related to mechanical principles, and the direction of problem solving activities are forms of verbal instruction.

RELATED RESEARCH

demonstration

Investigators have studied the effectiveness of motion pictures, filmstrips, loop films, and pictures upon motor learning. Loop films are motion pictures placed upon the projector in a closed loop so that the sequence may be shown repeatedly without rewinding the film. Filmstrips are still pictures shown in a particular sequence. Activities used by investigators have included bowling, badminton, gymnastics, tumbling, and football.

Motion pictures. Lockhart (1944) found that subjects who were taught bowling through motion picture demonstration showed a more consistent rate of improvement than subjects who learned without motion picture study. She also found that the film was most valuable in the second stage of learning after the subjects had had some practice. During the first phase of the experiment, both groups of subjects were almost identical; then the experimental group continued improving while the control group hit a learning plateau.

Brown and Messersmith (1948) conducted a similar experiment related to the teaching of tumbling. The experimental group was shown motion pictures of expert performers during the fifth class period and of their own performance eight class periods later. They found that although the experimental group made the most progress, the difference between groups was not significant.

The effects of motion pictures and flash cards upon football play recognition time were compared by Londeree (1967). Forty-two male high school boys were placed into two equated groups based on intelligence and football experience. Motion pictures were taken of six football plays, and these same plays were diagrammed on flash cards. Each group was trained using one of the visual aids. Following a total learning period of 110 minutes, subjects were tested on play recognition time with a live offense running the plays. There were no differences between groups when they were compared on the basis of accuracy: however, the motion picture group was significantly better than the flash card group when they were compared on the basis of response time. The author indicated that the response time of the motion picture group was fast enough for them to react effectively in a game situation, whereas the flash card group did not react quickly enough.

Filmstrips.   Feinberg (1951) taught two classes in beginning badminton. A filmstrip was shown to the experimental group in addition to the conventional methods used with the control group. No significant differences were found between the groups.

Loop films.   The use of loop films by an inexperienced teacher was compared with the teaching effectiveness of an experienced teacher (Murnin, Hayes, and Harby, 1952). Four groups of college males were equated according to scores on the Metheny Test of Motor Educability, and were taught eight tumbling events. Although the film groups learned the skills, it was concluded that live teaching by the experienced teacher constituted the better method.

Nelson (1958) used slow motion loop films showing the use of the 7-iron in teaching beginning golf to college students, in addition to explanation and demonstration. An experimental group viewed the films for five minutes before practice and five minutes midway through practice daily for fifteen days. No differences were found between the performance of the experimental and control groups.

Gray and Brumbach (1967) studied the effectiveness of the daylight projection of loop films on badminton playing ability. Although previous studies involving loop films showed no differences between experimental and control groups, Gray and Brumbach employed the more recently developed Technicolor Instant Motion Picture Projector and the Magi-Cartridges. The experimental group improved significantly during the first five weeks of practice. Both groups improved significantly over the total ten-week period. Although the experimental group was significantly better than the control group at the midterm testing, this difference did not exist at the end of the experiment. The investigators concluded that the use of loop films hastened initial learning. They also pointed out that the experimental group was required to view the films during the first five weeks and that viewing was optional following this period.

Pictures. Jarvis (1967) employed self-instructive materials related to skills, stunts, and exercises practiced by fourth grade students. These materials included pictures and diagrams with written explanations. An experimental group improved significantly over a six-month period, whereas a control group showed no significant improvement.

manual assistance

Investigations related to the value of manual assistance are practically nonexistent. There are no investigations in which physical education activities have been employed, although this form of communication is used by physical educators, especially in activities such as tumbling and gymnastics.

Ludgate (1923) attempted to determine the value of manual assistance in learning a stylus maze. She found that such assistance did help the subjects to learn faster and that the group aided during only two practice trials was superior to groups receiving aid on up to sixteen trials. Subjects who had initial practice on their own gained the most from such assistance; if inserted at the later stages of learning, manual assistance was of no value.

Carr (1930) later conducted a similar experiment and found that the effectiveness of manual guidance decreases with the amount given. He also found that it was most effective after the subjects had explored the maze on their own.

verbal instruction

Investigations dealing with verbal instruction as a means of communication fall into two categories. A number of studies are related to knowledge of mechanical principles; others relate to understanding the nature of the task.

Mechanical principles. Judd (1905) taught students principles of light refraction related to striking a target submerged in varying depths of water. The students who had the instruction showed superiority in hitting the target as the depth of the water was changed when compared to those students who were required to rely completely on trial and error methods of adjustment.

Using equated groups, Mikesell (1962) found no significant differences between an experimental group which was taught to apply mechanical principles in a badminton class and a control group. Similar findings were reported by Cobane (1959) when beginning tennis was the motor activity. It was noted that although the experimental group had less actual practice time than the control group, there were no differences in level of skill.

Three investigations have involved an experimental group which completed instruction in mechanical principles prior to participation in sports activities. Broer (1955), using college women of low motor ability as subjects, found that when scores on skill and knowledge tests in badminton, bowling, and folk dancing were combined, subjects with previous instruction were superior to those who had not received such instruction. When scores were compared for each of the three activities, there were no significant differences between groups.

Using seventh grade girls as subjects, Broer (1958) found that an experimental group was equal to or better than a control group in volleyball, basketball, and softball skills. When scores on all skill tests were combined, the experimental group was superior to the control group, although the experimental group had had less instruction in the sports in order to learn the mechanical principles.

In the third study, Coleman (1968) reported that a prerequisite unit in movement education had no significant effect on improvement in bowling. College women were used as subjects.

Colville (1956) found that learning a mechanical principle did not materially affect the ability to learn a skill similar to the one in which that principle was introduced. Verbal instructions constituted the means of teaching the principles. She selected three principles and three motor skills, each utilizing one principle. Two comparable groups of college undergraduate students learned each of the skills. The experimental group learned the principle underlying the skill. Both groups then learned a new skill involving the same principle as the first without any instruction related to the principle. No significant differences were found between the two groups.

When swimming was the motor activity and related principles were taught to experimental groups, Garland (1960) reported no differences in performance in the elementary back stroke or the front crawl. In the breast stroke, however, the experimental group was superior to the control groups in form and endurance. Mohr and Barrett (1962) reported that an experimental group performed significantly better than a control group on tests of improvement in the front crawl sprint, side stroke power, and form in the front crawl, back crawl, and side stroke. Mechanical principles were presented in class and experimental subjects received in addition a list of principles related to a written analysis of each stroke. Control subjects received the written analysis of strokes but had no instruction related to mechanical principles.

Task understanding. Verbal instructions telling students what was expected of them in skill performance were given in two studies concerning speed and accuracy. Solley (1951) emphasized speed, accuracy, and speed and accuracy during the practice of a motor skill requiring both speed and accuracy. The verbal instructions directly affected performance, as subjects responded according to which factor was emphasized during initial instruction.

Subjects were high school boys selected by random sampling, and the objective was to strike a target with a striking instrument, using a thrusting movement. Three groups of subjects were used: group one devoted the first half of the time to emphasis upon speed; group two received initial emphasis upon accuracy; and group three received initial emphasis upon speed and accuracy. During the second half of the study, all groups received emphasis upon both speed and accuracy. The subjects were given fifteen trials per day, two days per week, for three weeks during each half of the study. During the equal emphasis period (the second half of the study) the accuracy group lost accuracy and gained in speed, the speed group gained in accuracy and lost speed slightly, and the speed and accuracy group lost slightly in accuracy and gained consistently in speed. Solley concluded that speed developed initially is readily transferred. Accuracy performances are variable and are lost when speed is increased. In skills in which speed is predominant, early emphasis should be based on speed. In skills involving both speed and accuracy, both should be equally stressed.

Using twenty-one tenth grade boys as subjects, Woods (1967) studied the effects of varied emphasis on speed and accuracy in learning the tennis forehand drive. He employed three experimental treatments: (1) initial instruction related to attainment of velocity with later instruction related to accuracy; (2) initial instruction related to accuracy and later instruction in velocity; (3) equal and simultaneous emphasis on speed and accuracy. Subjects received sixty trials during each of the twenty-four practice periods. When performance was measured in terms of both speed and accuracy, findings revealed that equal emphasis produced the best results, and that initial emphasis on accuracy was less desirable than initial emphasis on velocity.

communication compared

Few investigators have compared the various forms of communication, and some types of communication have not yet been compared with any others. Ruffa (1937) found that in learning selected motor skills, those subjects receiving instruction through motion pictures showed the most improvement, and that subjects receiving oral instruction improved more than subjects receiving no instruction. He used three groups of subjects equated as to age, height, weight, intelligence, and a pre-test in the five events which included a football throw, the broad jump, the shot put, the high jump, and the 100-yard dash.

Halverson (1949) compared three methods of teaching motor skills. She concluded that a kinesiological method involving the application of principles and a demonstration with verbal connection method were superior to mental practice and trial and error methods. A one-hand basketball shot was the motor skill.

Berlin (1959) investigated the effects of the following five teaching devices upon the early learning of five motor skills: (1) undirected trial and error practice, (2) repeated demonstration of the skill, (3) detailed and extensive verbal explanation of the skill, (4) selected visual aids, and (5) a balanced variety of the above. A total of 111 sophomore women subjects were randomly placed into five groups. The five variables were rotated during the teaching of the five skills so that each group was exposed to each variable. No two groups were exposed to the same variable during the learning of the same skill. Learning was evaluated by testing the subjects three times during their exposure to each skill. Berlin found that in three out of five skills, the group with undirected practice showed the highest mean score. The balanced variety group scored highest in two skills and lowest in a third. Two groups showed the lowest mean score in two different skills where the visual aid was the variable. Groups taught by verbal detail scored lowest two times. Groups taught by demonstration never showed the highest or lowest mean score. Berlin concluded that after initial opportunity for understanding, the beginner seems to be aided by (1) uninterrupted practice, and (2) varied teaching methods. Demonstration seems to provide aid for many learners, and verbal analysis and visual aids appear less valuable as major teaching emphases.

DISCUSSION

Research findings to date suggest that the physical educator can employ any method of visual or verbal communication in teaching beginning classes. In actual practice, this variety of methods is most administratively feasible. Available equipment and facilities have a direct bearing upon the choice of mode of communication. The nature of the activity and thus the teaching station also affect the type of communication selected by the teacher. The teacher's competencies and the students' past experience are other factors which might be considered.

demonstration

In studies dealing with the various forms of demonstration, most investigators have found no differences between groups taught with mechanical visual aids such as movies, loop films, and filmstrips and groups taught without such aids. These findings mean that any method of demonstration may be used.

The physical educator often teaches many different activities. It is unlikely that most teachers will be competent in the demonstration of all the skills they will teach. Although one investigation (Murnin, Hayes, and Harby, 1952) showed that the use of a visual aid by an inexperienced teacher was less effective than live teaching by an experienced teacher, the question of whether live teaching by the inexperienced teacher would be more effective than the use of a visual aid remains unanswered. If the teacher is unable to demonstrate correctly, the value of a live demonstration is negated and films might be selected as a more valuable teaching aid.

The Russian author Ozlin (1958) goes into theoretical detail regarding the values of demonstration in the instruction of sports techniques. The essence of his paper suggests that the learner begins to develop a kinesthetic feeling for the movement as he watches a demonstration before he ever attempts the movement. This sensory input, therefore, appears to evoke a neurological motor response. Ozlin's theory can probably be confirmed by most people who have attended a dance concert, baseball game, soccer match, or any other athletic event. One "feels" a response as one watches the performers. If such responses are evoked, it is important to have teaching demonstrations given by skilled performers.

The value of slow motion films might be questioned in light of Ozlin's theory. The learner who has no concept of the desired speed of a movement could be confused with only slow motion films to imitate. On the other hand, such films may allow the learner to grasp more of the detail once he has the feeling of the movement. Live slow motion demonstration, however, is a questionable means of communication inasmuch as the movement itself is changed in the attempt to slow it down.

Demonstration is often accompanied by verbal cues which direct the learner's attention to certain details of the motor act. In a study in which she observed the eye movements of subjects watching demonstrations, Mott (1954) found that subjects observed those body parts and movements that were important for initial performance without receiving specific cues. Although no investigations were specifically designed to study directing attention to details following initial performance, it may be that the learner is more ready for detail after he can produce the gross components of the movement. Highly skilled performers, for example, pay attention to minute details in an effort to achieve even greater proficiency.

The placement of verbal cues during the demonstration is worthy of consideration, although no research has been conducted to support observations. People generally look at the face of a person who is talking; thus, commenting while demonstrating might actually distract rather than direct attention. Comments following a demonstration tend to assume that all learners have observed the same thing. It would seem logical to give verbal cues preceding the demonstration and then allow the learner to concentrate on observation of the movement.

The suggested contradiction between the findings of Lockhart (1944) and Gray and Brumbach (1967) points out the need for further study. While movies appeared to be of greater value in later stages of learning bowling, and loop films of greater value in early stages of learning badminton, the interpreter of these findings must realize that conditions were dissimilar in the two studies. In the Lockhart study the activity was bowling and the motion pictures were shown throughout the entire unit, whereas in the Gray and Brumbach study the activity was badminton and subjects were required to view the loop films during the first half of the unit only.

The findings of these two studies, in which the data were analyzed in terms of two learning stages, suggest that the value of demonstration may differ during different stages of learning. Since beginners have generally been used as subjects in investigations dealing with communication, the value of demonstration and the value of several types of demonstrating remain unexplored for the more advanced performer.

manual assistance

Generalizations related to manual assistance arise from investigations in which the tasks were unlike those found in physical education activities. Manual assistance can take two forms. One consists of actually moving a body part through the desired path. This is difficult to do at the actual speed of most movements. The second form includes spotting techniques such as those used in gymnastics and tumbling. The importance of a study designed to evaluate spotting is questionable. The safety factors involved would preclude the use of a control group without spotters at initial stages of performance in skills where spotters are normally provided.

verbal communication

Three methods of verbal communication have been studied by investigators: detailed explanation of skilled movements, instructions related to the purpose of a skill, and the teaching of mechanical principles.

Verbal instructions which explain the purpose of a skill and inform the learner what is expected of him appear to have great value (Solley, 1951, and Woods, 1967). In studies in which verbal emphasis was placed on speed and accuracy, both important factors in projectile skills, equal emphasis yielded the best results. In sports that involve projectile skills, therefore, in addition to communication related to the form of the movement, the learner should be verbally instructed to practice with the goal of developing both speed and accuracy.

Studies related to verbal communication of mechanical principles show varying findings. When projectile skills involving striking were used as the motor task, experimental and control groups did not differ significantly (Cobane, 1959, and Mikesell, 1962). Considering the number of mechanical principles which affect performance in this type of skill, these results are not surprising. When swimming skills were employed (Garland, 1960, and Mohr and Barrett, 1962), knowledge of mechanical principles appeared to be valuable in skill development. In two studies (Broer, 1955 and 1958), combined scores on several activities favored experimental groups who had had pre-instruction related to mechanical principles. Although the superiority of verbal communication of mechanical principles is not conclusive, it should be noted that it was never detrimental, but was as good as or better than teaching without communicating mechanical principles.

The duration of investigations dealing with mechanical principles is short when compared with the number of years students are enrolled in physical education classes. Perhaps the ability to apply mechanical principles to performance is a skill which must be developed over a longer period of time. The AAHPER knowledge and understandings test which has been written for students in elementary and high schools and the accompanying manual should stimulate the teaching of mechanical principles at all ages. Even the first grade student can begin to learn these principles in his own terms. For example, rather than "follow through in the direction you want the ball to go," words such as "point your hand and arm at the target" are easily understood by young children.

Detailed verbal explanation of a skill appears to be the least effective means of verbal communication. This is understandable when one considers that most investigators use beginners as subjects. Some concept of the skill involved is essential to an understanding of the explanation. Even a physical educator would have difficulty in interpreting an explanation of a skill he had never seen. For example, ask several persons to attempt the following movement from its description and see how many movement variations are elicited. With the right side facing the target and the ball grasped in the right hand, swing the arm across the body in a frontal plane from a position of horizontal abduction through an arc of 270 degrees. Release the ball so that it travels to a high point of seven feet and lands twenty feet away. (See Figure 4.1 for an illustration of this movement.)

Two methods of communicating verbally remain unexplored. One of these methods is the use of cues. Cues can give the learner an idea of the feeling associated with the movement. For example, in tennis the student is instructed to "squeeze" the racket at the moment of impact with the ball. Sometimes cues are related to the sound associated with the movement, such as the "swish" of the racket in badminton. Another method of teaching through verbal instruction is called problem solving. Although most often used in dance, it can also be used in the teaching of sports skills. In this method the student is directed by verbal suggestions and often finds himself performing a movement which otherwise might have seemed overwhelmingly complicated to him. Two investigators (Broer, 1958, and Garland, 1960) used the problem solving method of teaching mechanical principles. The studies, however, were designed to investigate the effects of the knowledge of mechanical principles rather than the problem solving approach. No studies were found in which this method of communication constituted the treatment variable.

communication compared

Comparison of methods of communicating supports the generalization that varied teaching methods should be employed. When one considers that a class is made up of many individuals with varying backgrounds, it is not surprising that no one method of communicating to a group is superior to any other method.

The teacher should analyze the nature of the activity before choosing the means of communication to be employed. The form of a movement may be more easily communicated through demonstration than detailed verbal explanation. A demonstration, however, is copied or imitated by the learner, and such imitation may be undesirable in creative activities such as dance. In watching a dance concert, one often becomes aware of "favorite movements" or "favorite techniques" that appear in many of the dances. In such activities it is important to encourage students to develop their own movements rather than to rely completely on imitation of the demonstration. Verbal communication such as that used in the problem solving method might produce more desirable results. In addition, the teacher should evaluate his own proficiency in choosing a method of communication. There are times when a loop film or movie is superior to an average demonstration.

GENERALIZATIONS

1. Motion pictures appear to be a valuable aid for many beginners.
2. There are no apparent differences between learning with or without the use of loop films or filmstrips.
3. Live demonstrations seem to provide aid for many beginners.
4. Manual assistance may be of value for learners after initial practice on their own if given during one or two trials in the early stages of learning.
5. Knowledge of mechanical principles may increase learning.
6. Understanding what is expected of them in performing a motor task is of value to beginners.
7. Detailed verbal instructions are of little value until the learner has the background necessary to understand them.
8. Varying methods of communication appear to be appropriate for beginners.

BIBLIOGRAPHY

Battig, William F. 1956. Transfer from verbal pretraining to motor performance as a function of motor task complexity. *J. Ed. Psychol.* 51:371–78.

Berlin, Pearl. 1959. Effects of varied teaching emphasis during early learning on acquisition of selected motor skills. Unpublished Ph.D. thesis, Pennsylvania State University.

Broer, M. R. 1955. Evaluation of a basic skills curriculum for women students of low motor ability at the University of Washington. *Research Quarterly* 26:15.

———. 1958. Effectiveness of a general basic skills curriculum for junior high school girls. *Research Quarterly* 29:379.

Brown, Howard, and Messersmith, Lloyd. 1948. An experiment in teaching tumbling with and without motion pictures. *Research Quarterly* 19:304.

Carr, Harvery. 1930. Teaching and learning. *J. Genet. Psychol.* 37: 189–218.

Cobane, Edith. 1959. A comparison of two methods of teaching selected motor skills. Unpublished Ph.D. thesis, Syracuse University.

Coleman, Dorothy. 1968. Effect of a unit of movement education upon the level of achievement in bowling. *Abstracts of Research Papers: AAHPER 1967 Convention.* Washington, D.C.: American Association for Health, Physical Education, and Recreation.

Colville, Frances. 1956. The learning of motor skills as influenced by a knowledge of general principles. Unpublished Ph.D. thesis, University of Southern California.

Feinberg, Ruth. 1951. The sound filmstrip as a teaching aid in learning badminton. Unpublished Master's thesis, University of Southern California.

Garland, I. L. 1960. Effectiveness of problem solving method in learning swimming. Unpublished Master's thesis, University of California, Los Angeles.

Gray, C. A., and Brumbach, W. B. 1967. Effect of daylight projection of loop films on learning badminton. *Research Quarterly* 38:562.

Halverson, Lolas E. 1949. A comparison of three methods of teaching motor skills. Unpublished Master's thesis, University of Wisconsin.

Jarvis, Lindle. 1967. Effects of self-instructive materials in learning selected motor skills. *Research Quarterly* 38:623.

Judd, C. H. 1905. Movement and consciousness. *Psych. Rev.* 7:199.

Lockhart, Aileene. 1944. The value of motion pictures as an instrumental device in learning a motor skill. *Research Quarterly* 15: 181.

Londeree, Ben R. 1967. Effect of training with motion pictures versus flash cards upon football play recognition. *Research Quarterly* 38:202.

Ludgate, Katherine E. 1923. The effect of manual guidance upon maze learning. *Psych. Monographs* 33:1:1–65.

Mikesell, Deloris. 1962. The effect of mechanical principle centered instruction on the acquisition of badminton skill. Unpublished Master's thesis, University of Illinois.

Mohr, D. R., and Barrett, M. E. 1962. Effect of knowledge of mechanical principles in learning to perform intermediate swimming skills. *Research Quarterly* 33:574.

Mott, Jane. 1954. Eye movements during initial learning of motor skills through visual demonstration. Unpublished Ph.D. thesis, University of Southern California.

Murnin, J. A.; Hayes, W.; and Harby, S. F. 1952. *Daylight projection of film loops as the teaching medium in perceptual motor skill training.* (SDC 269-7-26) Instructional Film Research Program, Pennsylvania State College.

Nelson, Dale O. 1958. Effect of slow motion loop films on the learning of golf. *Research Quarterly* 29:37.

Ozlin, N. G. 1958. Motor concepts in teaching sports technique. Translated by M. Yessis. *The Theory and Practice of Physical Culture* 21:6:746–51.

Ruffa, Edward J. 1937. Experimental study of motion pictures as used in the teaching of certain athletic skills. *Athletic Journal* 37:20.

Solley, William H. 1951. Speed and accuracy as directives in motor learning. Unpublished Ph.D. thesis, Indiana University, 1951.

Woods, John B. 1967. The effect of varied instructional emphasis upon the development of a motor skill. *Research Quarterly* 38:132.

4

Knowledge
of Results

Information related to performance which is available to the performer during the learning period is referred to as feedback. Servomechanisms which mediate the integration of feedback from internal sensory receptors were discussed in Chapter 1. Ammons (1956) points out that there is always some intrinsic knowledge available to the performer. This feedback is available during the performance of the skill. Additional feedback may be provided following performance and is referred to as *knowledge of results*. Annett and Kay (1956) suggest that this additional knowledge of results is important because it helps the learner identify the intrinsic or kinesthetic information which is available during performance. The term *knowledge of results* as used in this chapter encompasses other terms found in the literature, such as "knowledge of performance" (Ammons, 1956), "information feedback" (Archer, Kent, and Mote, 1956) "supplemental information" (Bilodeau, 1952), and "augmenting cues" (Karlin and Mortimer, 1963).

Investigations of the effects of knowledge of results upon the learning of motor skills vary in many ways. In general, the tasks which have been used can be categorized into those in which the subject could not see what he was doing and those in which he could see. Knowledge of results supplied by the investigator during the learning of a visual task augments that which is available through vision. Although there is some overlapping, the review of studies presented in this chapter is divided into those in which subjects could not see and those in which they could see. Within these categories, investigations are classified according to conditions under which knowledge of results was varied.

RELATED RESEARCH

nonvisual tasks

Most of the nonvisual tasks utilized by investigators involve fine motor activity. Line drawing, knob turning, and lever positioning have been used most frequently. The findings of these studies will be summarized. Only two investigators used large ballistic throwing movements. The related research is divided into sections according to the way in which knowledge conditions were varied.

One source of variation involves a comparison of different types of knowledge of results. In some studies the amount of practice with knowledge has provided a source of variation. A number of studies have dealt with the delay of knowledge over periods of seconds or trials. In addition to conditions related to type, amount, and delay of knowledge, in several instances investigators have also been interested in performance following the removal of knowledge of results.

Type of knowledge. Investigations have been designed to study the effect of the type of knowledge of results upon performance. The nonvisual tasks used involved fine motor activity. It appears that the more information available to the subject, the higher the level of skill acquisition (Ross, 1933, and Trowbridge and Cason, 1932). For example, in line drawing tasks simple "right-wrong" information was of greater value than no information but was less effective than information related to the extent and direction of the error. When the type of information consisted of a performance score or incentive, the initial level of motivation of the subjects has been held responsible for the effects of knowledge of results. Where it was assumed that all subjects had high levels of motivation, knowledge conditions produced no significant effects when compared with no-knowledge conditions

(Crafts and Gilbert, 1935, and Ross, 1933). Wireman (1960) compared four approaches to increasing physical fitness as measured by the Indiana Motor Fitness Test. Two teaching methods were varied under knowledge and no-knowledge conditions. Fitness improved under knowledge conditions regardless of whether the teaching methods included calisthenics, sports, and games, or just sports and games. Subjects included forty-eight male college students. Investigations related to type of knowledge generally support the finding that performance improves under conditions where knowledge is available and performance deteriorates when knowledge is withdrawn (Denny, 1946; MacPherson, Dees, and Grindley, 1948; Pierson and Rasch, 1964; Thorndike, 1927).

Amount of knowledge. Investigations in which the amount of practice with knowledge of results was the primary treatment variable differ markedly in design. Tasks varied from simple line drawing to much more complex fine motor tasks. Because of the differences, it is difficult to generalize about the findings of the related investigations. It appears that learning is a function of the number of practice trials with knowledge of results (Baker and Young, 1960; Bilodeau and Bilodeau, 1958; Bilodeau, Bilodeau, and Schumsky, 1959; Eaton, 1935).

Delay of knowledge. Delay of knowledge of results has been studied by a number of investigators. Delay refers to the amount of time which elapses between a trial and the knowledge of results. An experiment involving a large ballistic movement was conducted by Lorge and Thorndike (1935). Four groups of subjects were instructed to toss balls back over their heads at an unseen target. Knowledge of results was given in the form of a score which indicated where the ball hit the target. The treatment variables included (1) no knowledge, (2) immediate knowledge, (3) knowledge after delays of one, two, four, and six seconds, and (4) knowledge after the next throw. No differences were found between immediate knowledge and delays up to six seconds. No improvement was shown when knowledge was given after an intervening throw and the no-knowledge group showed a decrease in accuracy. It was concluded that learning does not take place without knowledge of results.

Using a similar movement, Alexander (1951) had subjects throw darts over a screen at an unseen target. Knowledge of results was provided by a panel of lights showing where the darts had landed.

Periods of delay were zero, two, four, eight, and sixteen seconds. There were thirty learning trials and five trials in which subjects were asked to predict where the darts had landed before the lights flashed on the panel. No evidence of differential learning was found.

McGuigan (1959) pointed out that delay is usually confounded with at least one other variable during experimentation. The length of the interval between trials, the length of the delay period, and the post-knowledge delay period are variables which investigators have attempted to isolate. The majority of the evidence related to delays of seconds reveals that delay is not an important variable. When knowledge of results was delayed over intervening trials, immediate knowledge was found to favor acquisition of skill.

visual tasks

Tasks in which the subject can see the results of his performance differ from those in which he cannot see. In investigations related to knowledge of results, knowledge supplied by the investigator augments that which is already available to the learner through vision. Tracking tasks have been employed in the majority of the studies which fall into this category. Although knowledge of results has been varied in ways similar to the ways in which it was varied in studies falling in the nonvisual category, the investigations have been classified as to whether knowledge of results was coincident or non-coincident with performance. Coincident knowledge occurs simultaneously with performance whereas non-coincident knowledge follows performance.

Coincident knowledge. Knowledge conditions coincident with performance on tracking tasks included the use of clicks (Reynolds, 1951; Reynolds and Adams, 1953; Williams and Briggs, 1962), tones (Archer, Kent, and Mote, 1956; Archer and Namikas, 1958), and lights (Bilodeau, 1952). When clicks or lights were used, performance increased with the augmented knowledge; when tones were used, no differences were found. This led to the hypothesis that the type of knowledge influenced performance. Unfortunately, no investigation was found which was designed to study this problem.

Removal of augmented knowledge was accompanied by a decrease in performance (Archer, Kent, and Mote, 1956; Bilodeau, 1952). In comparison with massed practice, distributed practice produced better performance (Reynolds, 1951). When the time on target required to produce a reinforcing click was varied, an intermediate difficulty level appeared to facilitate improvement (Reynolds and Adams, 1953).

It is interesting to note that whereas the studies in the nonvisual category employed knowledge of results primarily related to errors, all of the studies in the visual category employed knowledge of results related to correct performance. Only one investigation (Williams and Briggs, 1962) was designed to study on-target versus off-target information. When performance was measured with no additional knowledge available to the subjects, the off-target practice group demonstrated the best performance. It was suggested that as the subjects in this group improved, the no-knowledge situation was approximated.

Non-coincident knowledge. Johnson (1961) investigated the effects of knowledge of results upon the learning of tennis. The Dyer Blackboard Test of tennis ability was employed as a pre-test and a post-test. Two tennis classes were used, one as a control group and the other as an experimental group. Practice situations which could be objectively scored were used. Scores were recorded for the experimental group in such a way that the subjects could see the results of their performance for each day as well as the scores made by other subjects in the group. There were no differences found between the two groups. Johnson suggested that this might be due to a high level of motivation in both classes.

Howell (1956) used a sprint start as the motor task. Subjects in the experimental group were shown a force time graphic analysis of each start and were allowed to compare this to an ideal graph. During the first three days, there were no differences between experimental and control groups. During the remaining nine days, however, the experimental group performed significantly better.

Malina (1963) compared four groups who had practiced the baseball throw under four different knowledge conditions. One group received knowledge related to both the speed and accuracy of each trial. The subjects could see where the ball landed on a target and were also told the time of the flight. Subjects in an accuracy group could see where the ball landed; visual and verbal information related to the flight of the ball, however, was withheld. A speed group was told the time of the flight and all visual information was withheld. A no-knowledge group was denied any information. It was found that when the performance of each group was measured in relation to speed and accuracy (important factors in skills involving projectiles), it was directly related to the type of knowledge provided. Unfortunately, none of these conditions approximated the typical classroom situation in which students can see the flight of a projectile and where it lands without being told the speed of the projectile.

Bell (1966) studied the effects of varying knowledge of results during the practice of the badminton long serve in a classroom situation. Subjects in the experimental groups were instructed to serve so that the shuttlecock would travel over a rope fifteen feet from the floor and land in the appropriate area of the court between the baseline and the doubles long-service line. Subjects served twenty times daily for eight days. Under one condition, subjects were asked to correct the error committed on each trial. Two conditions emphasized the most common error committed during twenty trials. Under one condition the direction of the common error was emphasized, and under the other condition both the extent and direction of the common error was emphasized. A control group practiced without the visual aid or additional emphasis on knowledge of results.

All groups improved in performance during the practice period. No significant differences were found between groups on a post-test and retention test with the rope removed from the situation. One wonders whether the experimental groups actually attempted to correct errors in accordance with the directions given them. On the other hand, all subjects could have availed themselves of the same information even though they were not specifically directed to do so.

Bell (1968) designed a novel handball toss for use in a second study (see Figure 4.1). Two groups of college students practiced the skill under visual or verbal knowledge conditions. Subjects in the visual group could see whether each toss met the requirements of the skill, and subjects in the verbal group were blindfolded and given verbal information related to height and accuracy following each toss. Subjects practiced the toss twenty times daily for eight days. A pretest and a post-test were given under visual conditions. Although the visual group improved significantly, there were no significant differences between the groups on a post-test.

Robb (1968) found that subjects who practiced a tracking task with coincident visual feedback learned the task better than subjects who practiced without visual feedback and with terminal knowledge of results. The significant improvement of the visual group

Figure 4.1 Novel Handball Toss

in Bell's study might indicate a trend which would reflect Robb's findings. In comparing these studies, however, consideration must be given to the differences in the motor task and the nature of the criterion test. Whereas subjects in Bell's study were tested under visual conditions, subjects in Robb's study were tested without visual feedback.

Plese (1968) used fifty-four matched pairs of junior high school students in a study designed to compare a conventional method of teaching gymnastics (including demonstration, verbal explanation, instructor analysis, and correction) with the same method supplemented by television videotape instant replay. The experimental group performed significantly better than the control group after seven weeks of practice.

Using two groups of ten varsity baseball players, Watkins (1963) attempted to determine whether viewing motion pictures of their batting would decrease the batting faults of the experimental group. Subjects in the experimental group viewed their films once a week for a period of five weeks. Instruction was related to the correction of faults. The experimental group decreased the number of faults significantly whereas the control group did not. Differences between means for the five-week period favored the experimental group.

Investigations utilizing fine motor skills in this category are few in number and diverse in purpose, making comparisons relatively difficult. Non-coincident information in three investigations (Flieshman and Parker, 1962; Goldstein and Rittenhouse, 1954; Karlin and

Mortimer, 1963) was error information; in the other three investigations (Johnson, 1961; Smode, 1958; Stone and Lynn, 1951), it consisted of performance information. In the Goldstein-Rittenhouse and Karlin-Mortimer Studies, in which non-coincident error information was compared with coincident visual or auditory information, the former elicited higher performance ẅhen knowledge was removed. This finding appears to agree generally with theories suggested under other classifications; that is, learning conditions which are similar to no-knowledge conditions emphasize cues inherent in the task. Smode's findings, however, indicate that coincident information had a motivating effect which produced better performance than non-coincident information. In this study, however, performance was measured during the knowledge condition and furthermore, the non-coincident information consisted of a performance score rather than an error score.

DISCUSSION

There are essentially two types of feedback available to the learner of a motor skill. Internal feedback is related to kinesthesis. External feedback encompasses knowledge of results. All movements elicit internal feedback and the extent to which this is utilized cannot be controlled in investigations dealing with knowledge of results.

Knowledge of results is necessary for improvement in motor skills. Historically, Thorndike presented this conclusion based on a line drawing experiment in 1927. Since that time, many investigators have varied the type, amount, and delay of knowledge of results using various motor tasks. It is important to note that the majority of these investigations involved the use of nonvisual fine motor tasks such as line drawing, knob turning, and lever pushing. When subjects were allowed to see what they were doing, tracking tasks were most often used.

Physical education skills differ markedly from the tasks used by other investigators. In many physical education activities, skills are employed in which a certain amount of visual knowledge of results is inherent in the situation. Often the performer can see the results of his action. For example, he can see whether or not a ball goes into a basket, or a soccer goal is scored, or a pass reaches a teammate. Additional knowledge of results supplied in a practice situation or by the teacher augments that which is inherent in the task. Physical education activities involve the use of the whole body in a timed sequence, whereas the tasks employed by other investigators have generally required actions of the hand and arm.

It has been suggested that knowledge of results which has a directive effect is valuable to the learner. In one study (Johnson, 1961) involving tennis, the availability of performance scores had no significant effect upon an experimental group. A performance score is an indication of how well the learner is doing; it provides him with no directive information. In another study (Malina, 1963), students were given knowledge of results related to speed, accuracy, and speed and accuracy. This directive information enabled them to improve performance on the basis of the condition under which they practiced.

This generalization is further supported by another investigation (Howell, 1956) in which subjects were allowed to compare a force time graph of their performance of a sprint start with an ideal graph. This means of supplying knowledge of results evidently provided information which was directive to the subjects, since their performance was superior to that of a control group.

When the badminton long serve was practiced with vision (Bell, 1966) under conditions which emphasized error information, no significant differences were found between experimental groups and a control group which practiced in a conventional manner. Furthermore, performance did not deteriorate when the augmented knowledge of results was removed from the situation. These findings do not contradict previous findings that knowledge of results is necessary for improved performance in motor skills. Rather, they indicate that the type of visual skill found in physical education contains considerable inherent information which is of value to the learner.

The question arises, however, whether knowledge of results related to the projectile actually directs the student's practice while learning complex motor skills. Such knowledge certainly appears to be a directive in learning simple motor skills. Imagine drawing lines while blindfolded. Even being told "right" or "wrong" would aid you in making an adjustment. You would try drawing a longer or shorter line. More information related to the nature of your error would give you more assistance in your trial and error process. Compare this with the many complex adjustments which can be made to modify the movement involved in a physical education skill. Any one of several movement errors may have the same effect upon a projectile. Therefore, two students could receive the same knowledge of results with different underlying causes. With a knowledge of kinesiology, the student might check his balance, facing, follow through, speed of movement, or angle of release until he obtained the desired result.

Have we equipped our students with the understandings necessary to make use of available information? Can knowledge of results related to a projectile become meaningful in terms of cause and thus help the learner to modify his movement appropriately? There appears to be a gap between knowledge of results and its use as a directive. Since we cannot help each student in a class evaluate every trial in skill learning, it is important that we be concerned not only with the initial teaching of the motor skill, but with the skill of translating knowledge of results into understanding of the cause. This skill must be developed through a continuous process.

The importance of knowledge related to the cause of an error is supported by investigations in which subjects could view their own performance. In these investigations, experimental groups were superior to control groups. In activities involving only the body, such as dance, swimming, or diving, the performer must usually rely on kinesthetic feedback or cues supplied by the teacher. The use of mirrors has been emphasized in the study of dance for many years, as it provides immediate visual feedback for the student. The performance situation is unlike the practice situation, however, in that no visual feedback is available and the performer must rely on internal feedback. From this standpoint the method of practice with mirrors may be questionable. Another means of providing feedback in such activities might be through instant television replay. Here the learner would practice under conditions similar to those under which he would perform, yet he would receive knowledge of results. Unfortunately, this method is not only expensive but time-consuming, especially in large classes. With the advances in technology, however, the physical educator should strive to incorporate some of these methods into his teaching.

The importance of concentration on internal feedback has often been questioned. It has been found that paying attention to cues inherent in a motor task will yield high levels of performance (Lavery, 1962). Physical education skills include vision as a means of receiving inherent cues; yet it is often asked whether practice without vision would allow the performer to concentrate on internal feedback. In one investigation (Robb, 1968), in which subjects practiced under visual and nonvisual conditions and were tested under nonvisual conditions, coincident visual feedback was found to be most effective. In another study (Bell, 1968), in which the testing was conducted under visual conditions, it was concluded that practicing with vision hastens initial learning. When one considers that, neurologically, all sensory input is integrated for motor output, it seems important to practice a skill under conditions like those under which it will be performed.

In summary, the use of performance scores as knowledge of results appears to elicit high levels of skill acquisition when they provide a motivating effect. Probably the most important factor in planning students' learning experiences is to provide them with a means of gaining insight into the movement adjustments necessary for improvement. At present, visual replication of their performance appears to be the most effective means of doing this, although there are other methods which remain virtually unexplored. One of these involves teaching the student to translate from the result to the cause. Another is the effectiveness of verbal cues supplied by the teacher.

GENERALIZATIONS

1. Knowledge of results is necessary for learning.

2. When knowledge of results is removed from the situation, performance deteriorates.

3. Knowledge of results which has a directive effect appears to be more useful to the learner than that which does not.

4. The self-motivation of the learner may interact with knowledge of results as an additional incentive.

5. Delay of knowledge of results over lapses of seconds does not affect performance.

6. Improved performance is a function of the amount of practice with knowledge of results.

7. Performance related to speed and accuracy is directly related

to the type of knowledge of results which is available to the learner.

8. Tasks which are visual in nature contain considerable inherent knowledge of results.

9. Visual aids related to showing the nature of the error appear to have value for the learner.

10. Knowledge conditions which approximate performance conditions appear to elicit the highest levels of performance.

BIBLIOGRAPHY

Alexander, L. T. 1951. Knowledge of results and the temporal gradient of reinforcement. *Am. Psychologist* 6:292.

Ammons, R. B. 1956. Effects of knowledge of performance: a survey and tentative theoretical formulation. *J. General Psychol.* 54: 279–99.

Annett, J., and Kay, H. 1956. Skilled performance. *Occup. Psychol.* 30:112–17.

Archer, E. J.; Kent, G. W.; and Mote, F. A. 1956. Effect of long-term practice and time-on-target information feedback on a complex tracking task. *J. Exper. Psych.* 51:103–12.

Archer, E. J., and Namikas, G. A. 1958. Pursuit rotor performance as a function of delay of information feedback. *J. Exper. Psychol.* 56:325–27.

Baker, C. H., and Young, Phyllis. 1960. Feedback during training and retention of motor skills. *Canad. J. Psychol.* 14:257–64.

Becker, P. W.; Mussina, C. M.; and Pearsons, R. W. 1963. Inter-trial interval, delay of knowledge of results, and motor performance. *Percept. and Motor Skills* 17:559–63.

Bell, V. L. 1966. Augmented knowledge of results related to constant and variable errors and its effect upon acquisition and retention of a gross motor skill. Unpublished Ph.D. thesis, University of Southern California.

———. 1968. Visual and verbal feedback and its effect upon acquisition and retention of a projectile skill. Unpublished study, California State College at Los Angeles.

Bilodeau, E. A. 1952. Some effects of various degrees of supplemental information given to two levels of practice upon the acquisition of a complex motor skill. *Research Bulletin* 52–15. Human Resources Research Center, Lackland Air Force Base, San Antonio, Texas.

Bilodeau, E. A., and Bilodeau, Ina McD. 1958. Variable frequency of knowledge of results and the learning of a simple skill. *J. Exper. Psychol.* 55:379–83.

————. 1958. Variation of temporal intervals among critical events in five studies of knowledge of results. *J. Exper. Psychol.* 55: 603–12.

Bilodeau, E. A.; Bilodeau, Ina McD.; and Schumsky, D. 1959. Some effects of introducing and withdrawing knowledge of results early and late in practice. *J. Exper. Psych.* 58:142–44.

Bilodeau, Ina McD. 1956. Accuracy of a simple positioning response with variation in the number of trials by which knowledge of results is delayed. *Am. J. Psychol.* 69:434–37.

Crafts, L. W., and Gilbert, R. W. 1935. The effect of knowledge of results on maze learning and retention. *J. Ed. Psychol.* 26: 177–87.

Denny, M. R. 1946. The role of secondary reinforcement in a partial reinforcement learning situation. *J. Exper. Psychol.* 36:373–89.

Eaton, M. T. 1935. A study of latent learning. *J. Exper. Psychol.* 18:683–707.

Elwell, J. L., and Grindley, G. C. 1938. The effect of knowledge of results on learning and performance. I: A co-ordinated movement of the two hands. *Brit. J. Psychol.* 24:39–53.

Flieshman, E. A., and Parker, James F., Jr. 1962. Factors in the retention and relearning of perceptual motor skill. *J. Exper. Psychol.* 64:215–26.

Goldstein, M., and Rittenhouse, C. H. 1954. Knowledge of results in acquisition and transfer of a gunnery skill. *J. Exper. Psychol.* 48:187–96.

Howell, M. T. 1956. Use of force time graphs for performance analysis in facilitating motor learning. *Research Quarterly* 27:12–22.

Johnson, Joan. 1961. The effect of knowledge of results on the learning of tennis. Unpublished research project, University of Southern California.

Karlin, Lawrence, and Mortimer, R. G. 1963. Effect of verbal, visual, and auditory augmenting cues on learning a complex motor skill. *J. Exper. Psychol.* 65:75–79.

Lavery, J. J., 1961. Retention of some simple motor skills as a function of type of knowledge of results. Unpublished Ph.D. thesis, l'Universite de Montreal. Also (1962) *Canad. J. Psychol.* 16: 300–311.

Lavery, J. J., and Suddon, Florence H. 1962. Retention of simple motor skills as a function of the number of trials by which KR is delayed. *Percept. and Motor Skills* 15:231–37.

Lorge, I., and Thorndike, E. L. 1935. The influence of delay in the after-effect of a connection. *J. Exper. Psychol.* 18:186–94.

Macpherson, S. J.; Dees, Valerie; and Grindley, G. C. 1948. The effect of knowledge of results on learning and performance. II: Some characteristics of very simple skills. *Quart. J. Exper. Psychol.* 1:68–78.

Malina, Robert. 1963. Performance changes in a speed-accuracy task as a function of practice under different conditions of information feedback. Unpublished Ph.D. thesis, University of Wisconsin.

McCormack, P. D., and McElheran, W. G. 1963. Follow-up of effects on reaction time with partial knowledge of results. *Percept. and Motor Skills* 17:565–66.

McGuigan, F. J. Delay of knowledge of results: A problem in design. *Psychol. Rep.* 5 (1959):241–43.

Pierson, W. R., and Rasch, P. J. 1964. Effect of knowledge of results on isometric strength scores. *Research Quarterly* 35:313–15.

Plese, Elliot R. 1968. Comparison of videotape replay with a traditional approach in the teaching of selected gymnastic skills. *Abstracts of Research Papers: AAHPER 1968 Convention.* Washington, D.C.: American Association for Health, Physical Education, and Recreation.

Reynolds, B. 1951. Motor performance as a function of reinforcement and spacing of trials. (Abstract) *Am. Psychologist* 6:289.

Reynolds, B., and Adams, J. A. 1953. Motor performance as a function of click reinforcement. *J. Exper. Psychol.* 45:315–20.

Robb, Margaret. 1968. Feedback and skill learning. *Research Quarterly* 39:175–84.

Ross, C. C. 1933. The influence upon achievement of a knowledge of progress. *J. Ed. Psychol.* 24:609–19.

Ryan, F. J., and Bilodeau, E. A. 1962. Countertraining of a simple skill with immediate and 1-week delays of informative feedback. *J. Exp. Psychol.* 63:19–22.

Smith, A. H. 1963. Effects of continuous and intermittent feedback on precision in applying pressure. *Percept. and Motor Skills* 17:883–89.

Smode, A. F. 1958. Learning and performance in a tracking task under two levels of achievement information feedback. *J. Exper. Psychol.* 56:297–303.

Stone, G. R., and Lynn, J. O. 1951. Motor performance of children as a function of inverting their reported scores. *J. Genet. Psychol.* 78:97–103.

Suddon, F. H., and Lavery, J. J. 1962. The effect of amount of training on retention of a simple motor skill with 0- and 5-trial delays of knowledge of results. *Canad. J. Psychol.* 16:312–17.

Thorndike, E. L. 1927. The law of effect. *Am. J. Psychol.* 39:212–22.

Trowbridge, Margery, and Cason, H. 1932. An experimental study of Thorndike's theory of learning. *J. General Psychol.* 7:245–60.

Watkins, David L. 1963. Motion pictures as an aid in correcting baseball batting faults. *Research Quarterly* 34:228–33.

Williams, Alton C., and Briggs, George E. 1962. On-target versus off-target information and the acquisition of tracking skill. *J. Exper. Psychol.* 64:519–25.

Wireman, Billy O. 1960. Comparison of four approaches to increasing physical fitness. Part I. *Research Quarterly* 31:658–66.

part three
MOTOR OUTPUT

Part three of this book is devoted to the research related to the effects of practice upon motor output. Chapter 5 deals with massed and distributed practice, whole-part practice, and transfer. Chapter 6 is concerned with conceptualizing techniques and their effect on motor output. The factors which influence retention are presented in Chapter 7.

5

Practice Conditions

The question of how practice of a gross motor skill can be structured to facilitate the learning of that skill has received the attention of a number of investigators. Answers have been sought to questions in three general areas: massed and distributed practice; whole-part practice; and practice yielding transfer to related tasks. Much of the research has used tasks unlike those found in physical education activities, and this research has stimulated investigations in the practice of gross motor skills.

MASSED AND DISTRIBUTED PRACTICE

Massed practice may be defined as practice which is continuous and uninterrupted with intervals of rest. *Distributed practice* consists of a number of trials interrupted by time intervals. There are several problems in designing and comparing research on the question of which of these types of practice is most valuable. Among them are questions related to the duration of the practice period, the length of rest periods, the activity between practice periods, the interaction between the type of skill and the method used, and the interaction between the skill level of the performer and the method of practice.

related research

In 1960, Mohr reported that forty-five studies related to massed and distributed practice were found in psychological literature. Forty had results favoring distributed practice, three favored massed practice, and two found no significant differences. A review of studies related to gross motor skills follows.

Niemeyer (1958) compared massed and distributed practice in volleyball and badminton, using male college students as subjects. Massed practice consisted of sixty minutes of practice twice a week; distributed practice consisted of thirty minutes of practice three times per week. When improvement was compared in volleyball, it was found that during later learning massed practice produced a higher mean score. When improvement was compared in badminton, it was found that during early learning distributed practice was significantly better than massed practice. There were no differences between methods when overall improvement was compared.

The rate of learning in college archery and badminton classes was investigated by Young (1954). Four days per week of practice was compared with two days per week for a total of nineteen meetings in archery and sixteen meetings in badminton. When scores and hits were compared for the two-day group and the four-day group in archery, there were significant differences in favor of four days per week. In badminton, on the wall volley and the short serve, significant differences favored the two-day group. There were no differences on the high clear.

Using eight groups of male adult subjects, Ryan (1965) studied the effects of varying rest intervals on stabilometer performance. Eleven thirty-second trials were given to all subjects. The varied rest periods were ten, twenty, thirty, and forty seconds. In addition, four groups were given a five-minute rest following the eighth trial. There were no significant differences between rest intervals on the first eight trials. There were no significant differences between groups on the last three trials.

Using the stabilometer and the ladder climb, Stelmach (1968) studied the effects of massed and distributed practice. Four groups of forty subjects were used. Two groups practiced each skill under different conditions for a total of eleven minutes. Massed practice consisted of eight minutes of uninterrupted practice followed by six 30-second practice trials interrupted by thirty seconds of rest. The distributed practice group had sixteen 30-second trials interrupted by thirty seconds of rest, a total of eight minutes of practice. This was followed by four minutes of rest and six 30-second trials interrupted by thirty seconds of rest. During the first eight minutes the massed practice group evidenced a reduction in performance level; however, following the four-minute rest there were no differences in performance due to condition. The amount of learning was the same, regardless of type of practice.

Male college seniors were randomly assigned to two groups of thirty-five by Knapp and Dixon (1950). One group practiced juggling for five minutes per day and the other group practiced fifteen minutes every other day. Practice continued until the subject reached the criterion of 100 consecutive catches. The score was the number of minutes required to reach the criterion. The five-minute per day group reached the criterion in significantly less time than the fifteen-minute group. The latter group, however, learned the skill in fewer practice periods, though the total number of minutes was greater.

Knapp, Dixon, and Lazier (1958) repeated this juggling experiment with high school boys. In this second experiment, the practice of both groups was interrupted by weekends. The five-minute per day group learned to juggle significantly faster than the other group.

Singer (1965) studied the effects of massed and distributed practice, using a motor task in which the subject stood behind the basketball free throw line and bounced the ball from the floor into the basket. Three groups of forty male college students were equated on a pre-test. One group practiced eighty continuous shots. A second group had twenty shots followed by a five-minute rest for a total of eighty shots. A third group rested twenty-four hours between each set of twenty shots. At the conclusion of the experiment, the twenty-four hour rest group performed significantly better than the other two groups. Following one month without practice, the two massed practice groups performed better than the twenty-four hour rest group.

An additive pattern of practice was studied by Harmon and Miller (1950). College women with no previous experience in billiards were placed into four groups. Group one practiced for nine sessions, three days per week for three weeks. Group two was the additive group; practice was held on days 1, 2, 3, 5, 8, 13, 21, 34, and 55 of the experiment. The days of practice were determined by adding the numbers of the previous two days of practice. Thus, days 1 and 2 indicated practice on day 3, days 2 and 3 indicated practice on day 5, and so on. Group three practiced daily for nine straight days. Group four practiced one day per week for nine weeks. Eleven set shots of increasing difficulty were developed for practice. The first five shots were practiced the first day. Thereafter, one shot was added and one shot dropped each practice day. Subjects had a total of fifty shots per day. The additive pattern was better than the three days per week pattern. The additive group showed a greater mean gain than the other three groups. One day per week was the poorest method. It was concluded that massed practice during initial practice is better than widely spaced practice.

discussion

It is difficult to generalize about massed and distributed practice, since the research findings are contradictory. One of the reasons for the contradictions is that definitions of massed and distributed practice are not consistent. In some studies (Singer, 1956, and Stelmach, 1968), massed practice refers to trials completely uninterrupted by rest. In other studies, practice was massed in terms of the number of minutes per day (Niemeyer, 1958; Knapp and Dixon, 1950; Knapp, Dixon, and Lazier, 1958), or the number of days per week (Young, 1954). In some studies distributed practice was interrupted by seconds (Ryan, 1965, and Stelmach, 1968), in others by days (Niemeyer, 1958; Singer, 1965; Young, 1954), and in others by weeks (Harmon and Miller, 1950).

When badminton was the motor task, distributed practice of thirty minutes three times per week was found to be better than ninety minutes of practice twice a week during an early learning period (Niemeyer, 1958). When two class meetings per week were compared with four class meetings per week, the former was better in learning badminton (Young, 1954). In the first study the amount of improvement was the criterion, whereas in the second study final performance was compared. When other activities were used as the motor tasks with the same practice schedules, the findings differed. In volleyball, ninety minutes of practice twice a week was better during later learning than thirty minutes of practice three days per week (Niemeyer, 1958). In archery, classes meeting four days per week were significantly better than classes meeting two days per week (Young, 1954). These findings suggest that there is an interaction between the nature of the activity and the type of practice which is best. This points out a need for research in massed and distributed practice using all types of activities found in physical education classes.

Distribution of practice implies the presence of rest intervals. In two studies related to balance (Ryan, 1965, and Stelmach, 1968), rest intervals were varied within a single day. In both of these studies there were no differences in performance related to the amount of rest. When practice was uninterrupted by rest and continued for eight minutes, performance decreased. Following a four-minute rest, however, there was no difference in performance compared with a group which had distributed practice. These findings might suggest that practice should be distributed within a single class period. The amount of distribution needs further study. In the normal physical education class, students take turns practicing which affords rest intervals. The number of trials which should be taken on each turn is also an important consideration. This might be considered relative massing. For example, there might be quite a difference between a one-trial turn and a five-trial turn interrupted by rest intervals. No studies have been designed to study this problem.

The length of the daily practice period was studied, using juggling as the motor skill (Knapp, Clyde and Dixon, 1950). It was found that a five-minute period of practice daily was better than fifteen minutes of practice daily. This concept is supported by the study in which a novel basketball skill was used (Singer, 1965). This finding may have implications for the planning of daily lessons in physical education. Perhaps during a unit in an activity, shorter periods of daily practice of a particular skill would be more effective than practicing a single skill for half of a class period. The amount of equipment available should also be considered in planning classes, as it affects the amount of practice each student receives during a given time. Every effort should be made to have enough equipment so that class time may be spent in practice.

The additive pattern used in one study (Harmon and Miller, 1950) suggests another means of massing and distributing practice. According to the findings, massing practice during early learning and then distributing practice later can be effective in learning. In physical education, the number of classes per week is usually pre-determined.

In teaching a new skill, however, practice in the skill can be additive even though the days in class are fixed. Flexible scheduling of physical education classes will afford the physical educator greater possibilities for distributing or massing practices. The results of research in specific activities should serve as a guide in program planning.

GENERALIZATIONS

1. The effect of distribution of practice over a period of days interacts with the nature of the activity.
2. The duration of rest intervals within a practice session does not appear to affect performance.

WHOLE-PART PRACTICE

The practice of a *whole* may be defined as the practice of either a total skill or a total activity. If a whole is a total skill, then *parts* are defined as the elements which make up the whole, and practice consists of practicing these elements separately before combining them into a whole. These elements or parts may vary in size depending upon individual definition. If a whole is a total activity, then parts are usually defined as the skills which are involved in the activity, and these are practiced separately. *Progressive-part* learning is defined as the learning of part one and then part two, combining these, learning part three, combining all three parts, and so on until the whole is learned. The related research consists of comparative investigations of these methods. Much variation arises from differences in the definition of whole and part.

related research

Kimball (1934) studied the effectiveness of teaching basketball using part and whole methods. Seventy-eight male high school students were used as subjects. In the whole method, subjects scrimmaged daily. In the part method, fundamentals were practiced separately. During the last half of the eight-week period, the part method consisted of half drill and half scrimmage. Improvement in five skills was the dependent variable. The part method was the best for the short shot, the long shot, footwork, passing, and speed in passing. In foul pitching the whole method was better.

Niemeyer (1958) studied part and whole methods of teaching swimming, badminton, and volleyball. In badminton and volleyball, whole learning consisted of learning all the skills in the activity simultaneously from the beginning, and part learning involved learning the skills separately and then combining them. In swimming, the part method consisted of practicing the parts of a stroke separately whereas the whole method involved practicing each stroke as a whole. In badminton and volleyball during the early learning period, skills were practiced separately in drills for the part method and practiced in game situations for the whole method. During the late learning period both groups played round robin tournaments. A total of 336 male college students participated in the study. It was found that the whole method was best for teaching swimming. In badminton, the whole method was better than the part method in late learning. The part method was significantly better than the whole method during the early, late, and total learning periods in learning volleyball.

Hause (1944) used two equated groups of junior high school boys to study the effectiveness of a progressive-part and a whole method of teaching basketball shooting skills. At the end of five weeks the whole-method group who practiced all shots continuously was better than the other group. At the end of ten weeks the progressive-part group was better.

Using ninth grade boys, Cross (1937) studied three methods of teaching basketball. In the whole method subjects played basketball. In a minor-game method subjects played dodgeball, indoor baseball, volleyball, and relays. A whole-part method practiced shooting, passing, and moving skills. Passing and catching were learned best by the whole method. Skills of intermediate complexity such as jumping, starting and stopping, and pivoting were learned best by the minor-game method. The more complex skills were learned best by the whole-part method.

The whole method of teaching gymnastics and tumbling was compared with the whole-direct-repetitive method by Wickstrom (1958). In the whole-direct-repetitive method the stunt was described in detail two times. Then the first part of the stunt was demonstrated and practiced, the first and second parts demonstrated and practiced, and so on until the whole stunt was being practiced. The amount of time necessary to learn the stunt was the criterion. Twenty-seven subjects were divided into two experimental groups. On the basis of performance scores there were no significant differences. There were no differences in rates of learning the shoulder balance and the front heel upstart to side seat. The whole-direct-repetitive method seemed best for the handspring, and the whole method best for the other seven stunts. The only difference significant at the .05 level of confidence favored the whole method of practicing the back roll snap down.

Whole and part methods of learning to juggle were studied by Knapp and Dixon (1952). Male college students were placed into matched pairs on the basis of athletic experience. All subjects practiced daily for five minutes. The criterion was 100 consecutive catches. The dependent variable was the number of minutes of practice necessary to reach the criterion. The whole method consisted of practicing with all three balls at once. In the part method the movement was practiced without balls and then the three balls were added one at a time. The whole method was found to be superior.

Purdy and Stallard (1967) studied part-whole and whole methods of practice and their effect upon the full swing in golf as measured by distance and accuracy. Fifty-six college women enrolled in four beginning golf classes were the subjects. Group A used the part-whole method with an overlapping grip. Group B used the part-whole method and a ten-finger grip. Groups C and D used the whole method with the overlapping and ten-finger grips respectively. The part-whole method of practice involved learning a one-quarter swing, a half swing, and then a full swing, whereas the whole method involved practicing the full swing. Subjects practiced for fourteen class periods. There were no differences between methods or grips on a 5-iron test for distance. On a ninety-yard test for accuracy the whole method was significantly better than the part-whole method, and there were no differences between grips. When distance and accuracy scores were combined, the whole method was significantly better than the part-whole method.

DISCUSSION

The study of whole and part learning has its origins in psychology. The Gestalt theory of learning holds that the learner perceives a whole

(Bigge and Hunt, 1968). A whole is organized, and is more than a collection of parts. A conflict arises in defining the word "whole" in terms of physical education activities, since a whole may be either a total skill or a total activity.

There is relatively little research related to whole and part methods of teaching physical education activities. The research varies considerably in design and in definition of whole and part. Where whole methods have been defined as the playing of the game (Cross, 1937; Kimball, 1934; Niemeyer, 1958), the measure of performance has been the measure of one or more of the parts. These parts might also be considered wholes which could be broken into parts. There is no research available in which the total game whole method of teaching has been evaluated in terms of game performance.

In team sports, the part method of teaching appears to result in better performance on skills (Kimball, 1934, and Niemeyer, 1958). In this method a part consists of a skill, whereas the whole method is a game approach to learning skills. In the studies, the whole or game was also practiced by the part method groups. In one study (Hause, 1944), the whole method was defined as practicing several basketball shots continuously. This method resulted in better performance than a progressive-part method of practicing the shots. The skills which are necessary in team sports were not considered wholes by any investigators. Thus, there is no evidence concerning whole versus part methods of teaching these skills and their elements.

It may be generalized that the whole method of teaching individual sports is better than the part method, although both definitions of whole and part were used in investigations in individual sports. When badminton was used, the whole method consisted of playing the game (Niemeyer, 1958). In swimming, the whole method consisted of practicing a total stroke in contrast to practicing its parts (Niemeyer, 1958), and in golf the whole method consisted of practicing the total stroke (Purdy and Stallard, 1967). In juggling (Knapp and Dixon, 1952), the whole method was the total skill involving three balls, in contrast to a part method in which balls were added one at a time. Thus in three instances involving swimming, golf, and juggling, the whole was equivalent to the part used in team sport activities. In the three activities in which a skill was broken into parts (Niemeyer, 1958; Knapp and Dixon, 1952; Purdy and Stallard, 1967), practice of the skill under whole conditions yielded the best performance.

There is no research related to the type of practice and its interaction with level of skill. Often the advanced performer practices a part of a skill, paying attention to certain details, which suggests a whole-part-whole method of practice.

Based on the research to date, it appears that skills should be taught as whole units. It also appears that skills should be practiced separately as wholes before they are practiced in game-like situations.

GENERALIZATIONS

1. Skills found in team games such as volleyball and basketball should be practiced separately rather than in game situations.
2. Skills should be practiced as whole units.

TRANSFER

The effect of the practice of a skill upon performance of another skill is referred to as *transfer*. *Positive transfer* means that performance of the second skill is facilitated. *Negative transfer* means that performance of the second skill is interfered with. The relatively few studies of transfer which involve gross motor skills differ considerably in purpose and design. Some of the questions investigators have sought to answer concern transfer from simple skills to more complex skills and the reverse, transfer from one skill to a skill with similar elements, and teaching for transfer. The reader is also referred to the chapter on communication (Chapter 3) which presents the related research dealing with mechanical principles; the discussion of transfer includes concepts derived from this area of concern.

related research

Task complexity.   Riveness (1967) used a novel shuffleboard task to study transfer effects. The task was varied by changing the target distance. The tasks were labeled A, B, C, E, F, and G, with A representing the shortest and G the longest distance. Distance D was the transfer task. Nine groups of twenty male college students were used. Groups practiced according to the following schedule.

   I   30 trials on tasks A, B, C
  II   45 trials on tasks B, C
 III   90 trials on task C
 IV   30 trials on tasks E, F, C
  V   45 trials on tasks E, F
 VI   90 trials on task E
VII   30 trials on tasks A, B, C, E, F, G
VIII   45 trials on tasks B, C, E, F
 IX   90 trials on tasks C, E

When transfer effects on task D were studied significant amounts of transfer for groups I and VI were revealed. Thus multiple task practice was better for the easy tasks (shorter distance) and single task practice was better for the more difficult (longer distance) tasks.

Scannell (1968) studied the transfer of accuracy when practice conditions involved the use of targets which were smaller than the test target, a point in the center of the test target, larger than the test target, and identical to the test target. One skill used was dart throwing. On the basis of a pre-test, 190 male college students were placed into four groups. Each group practiced twenty-five throws per day for ten days using one of the alternate targets. On the succeeding two days, subjects threw twenty-five times per day at the test target. A second skill used was the softball throw. For eight days, 128 subjects practiced twenty-five times per day. The post-test consisted of twenty-five trials on the test target. There were no significant differences in post-test performance which could be attributed to varying target size during practice. Skill level demonstrated on the pre-test did not interact with any of the practice conditions.

Using archery as the motor task, Singer (1966) studied the effects of transfer from an easy or hard difficulty level defined by distance to an intermediate difficulty level. A total of fifty-eight college students enrolled in three archery classes were the subjects for this investigation. Each group practiced for five class periods. One group practiced at a distance of ten yards, the second group at twenty-five yards and the third group at forty yards. The groups were tested on the basis of four ends during the sixth class period. There were no significant differences between groups. The ten-yard group was tested at the 20, 25, 30, and 40-yard lines. The twenty-five yard group remained at the 25-yard line and was then tested at the 30, 20, 40, and 10-yard lines. The forty-yard group was tested at the 30, 25, 20, and 10-yard lines. No differences were found between groups at the 25-yard line which could be attributed to the difficulty level of the practice distance. There were no differences found at any yard line or on a Columbia junior round.

Similar elements. The Golf-O-Tron, a teaching aid, was used in a transfer study conducted by Chui (1965). The Golf-O-Tron employs color pictures of a golf course. The golfer responds to his position on the course, and by means of a computer the distance the ball would have traveled and the position of the ball on the course are shown following each shot. Chui compared the use of the Golf-O-Tron with the practice range method of practice. He also sought to determine whether improvement in the use of the 7-iron would transfer to the use of the 4-iron. Subjects included forty-seven men and thirty-eight women college students enrolled in beginning golf classes. All subjects received four class periods of instruction in the use of the 7-iron. They were then tested on the use of the 7-iron and the 4-iron. A four-week experimental period using the 7-iron was followed by a post-test. There were significant differences between males and females on the pre-test, but there were no differences between experimental and control groups. Post-test scores revealed a significant improvement which was related to method of practice. A significant improvement in the use of the 4-iron indicated that practice with the 7-iron had a positive transfer effect.

The effects of transfer between motor skills similar in perceptual components were studied by Vincent (1968). Two practice tasks and two criterion tests involving similar perceptual components and dissimilar motor responses were designed for use in the study. In the dot task the subject held a blue pen in one hand and a red pen in the other. He followed a pattern of blue and red circles by placing a red dot in red circles and a blue dot in blue circles. The related criterion test consisted of a jump board with blue and yellow foot prints painted on it in a pattern. The subject hopped or jumped through the pattern placing his left foot on the blue prints and his right foot on the yellow prints. The second practice task consisted of sitting and kneeling balance on a beam 1¾ inches by 16 inches by 15 inches. The related criterion test was a standing one foot balance on a balance beam. Three groups of subjects were pre-tested on the criterion tests. Group one practiced balance twice a day for two weeks and the dot task three times a day for two weeks. Group two reversed the order of practice. Group three had isometric exercises three minutes per day. The criterion tests were given after two and four weeks of practice. There were no significant differences among groups on a speed measurement of performance on the jump board. On the two-week criterion test, the group which had practiced the dot task was significantly better on the jump board test when performance was measured in terms of accuracy. On the four-week test, both experimental groups were superior to the control group on jump board accuracy. When speed and accuracy scores were combined, the only significant difference found favored the dot group over the control group on the two-week test. On the balance test at the end of two weeks, the group which had practiced the balance task was superior to the other two groups. On the four-week test, both groups were superior to the control group in balance. The author suggests that the perceptual components of the practice tasks were learned through practice and did transfer to the criterion test.

Cratty (1962) had thirty subjects practice on a small stylus maze for twelve trials, and then practice walking through an identical large maze. Another group reversed this procedure. The transfer from the large maze to the small maze was significant.

A second study (1962) was designed to study the transfer of small-pattern practice on a stylus maze to large-pattern performance walking through a maze thirty times larger. Four groups of twenty male university students were used. Group one had twelve practice trials on a stylus maze with a pattern similar to the one used in the locomotor maze. Group two practiced on a stylus maze with a pattern which was the reverse of the locomotor maze. Group three practiced on a stylus maze with an unrelated pattern. Group four had no small-pattern practice. Following the small-pattern practice, all groups had twelve trials on the large maze. All trials were taken while blindfolded. Negative transfer was observed initially by the group who had reverse small-pattern practice. Initial positive transfer was caused by similar small-pattern practice.

Teaching for transfer. Nelson (1957) used three pairs of skills in a study of transfer effects. They were the badminton wall volley and the tennis wall volley, the volleyball tap for accuracy and basketball tip for accuracy, and the track starting stance and the football starting stance. Three groups of subjects practiced under three different conditions: no transfer taught; teaching for transfer, including a verbal explanation of principles which could be applied to the paired skills; and teaching the pair of skills at the same time. The order of learning the skills was also varied. When the order of teaching the skills was compared, it was found that the track starting skill was learned significantly faster when it was taught prior to the football start. No other significant differences were found. When the interaction between method of practice and order of practice was compared, it appeared that teaching for transfer was effective when tennis preceded badminton. When the volleyball and basketball skills were learned separately, teaching for transfer was less effective than when they were learned alternately. Teaching for transfer was more effective in the football start when the paired skills were practiced separately than when they were practiced alternately. When badminton and tennis were learned alternately, there was more improvement under the no-transfer condition than when they were learned alternately under the teaching for transfer condition. It was concluded that skills involving similar patterns should not be practiced at the same time, and that teaching for transfer is not effective.

DISCUSSION

An understanding of the effects of transfer is important in program planning of physical education. If there were no transfer of any kind, the learner would have to start over with each activity presented. In reality, transfer is assumed to exist and this assumption underlies much of our educational process. We assume that practice of a skill will transfer to its use in a game situation. When we teach for understanding, we assume that basic concepts will transfer from one situation to another. Two major learning theories underlie many of our assumptions about transfer.

The identical elements theory of transfer is derived from the connectionist theory of learning. The connectionist or S-R theory holds that learning takes place through conditioning: specific responses are elicited by specific stimuli, and transfer takes place automatically when there are identical elements (Bigge and Hunt, 1968).

The theory of learning called operant conditioning explains learning as increasing the probability of the frequency of a response. This takes place by reinforcing a response through the use of a stimulus following the response. For example, the word "good" following a correct response can be a reinforcing stimulus. Responses containing similar elements are called a class of response. Increasing the future probability of a class of response is the concept underlying transfer. This is accomplished through reinforcement of the response element. New behavior is based upon the reinforcement of previous behavior (Skinner, 1957).

The Gestalt theory of learning is based on the concept that the learner tends to perceive the whole. Learning is considered a process of developing insights, which may be called generalizations. Transfer is based upon the desire to apply insights in new situations. This theory of transfer can be called a generalization theory in contrast to the identical elements theory (Bigge and Hunt, 1968).

The studies related to task complexity appeared to use tasks with similar elements. The target shooting task (Scannell, 1968) varied the size of the target although the response was identical. In the shuffleboard task (Riveness, 1967) and archery task (Singer, 1966), the variation in elements involved variations in distance. The findings appear to support the identical elements theory, although the evidence concerning transfer from simple to complex indicates a need for further research. Whereas in archery task complexity had no effect upon transfer, in the shuffleboard task multiple task practice was better in moving from simple to complex and single task practice was better in moving from complex to simple. In both studies complexity was based on distance. Differences in the findings might be due to the differences in the design of the experiments or they might suggest that the nature of the task interacts with transfer effects related to task complexity.

In other studies dealing with similar or identical elements it appears that positive transfer occurs in golf with the use of the 7-iron and the 4-iron (Chui, 1965). It would be interesting to know whether the results would be similar using a wood. The elements might be identical, yet the relative complexity of the use of a wood as compared to an iron might be an important factor.

Other studies dealing with elements (Cratty, 1962; Vincent, 1968) suggest that the perceptual elements can be identical although the tasks are unlike. These studies might fall into the categories of the identical elements transfer theory and the generalization theory. It is possible that transfer effects were due to insights developed during the learning of the first task and used in the performance of the second task.

Studies related to mechanical principles fall into the generalization theory of transfer. In essence a principle is a generalization which can be applied in a new situation. Findings do not entirely support the theory that understanding will affect performance on a new task. There are several factors which should be considered in appraising these findings. In the study by Judd (1905), the change in task involved changing the depth of a submerged target. The task certainly had some identical elements although the study was based on the generalization theory. Nelson (1957) and Colville (1956) used similar tasks to study the effects of principles. In both of these studies the use of principles did not affect performance on the new task, which contradicts the findings of Judd. In studies in which mechanical principles were taught prior to sports activities the results were also contradictory (Broer, 1955; Broer, 1958; Coleman, 1968). These contradictions suggest that the desire to use insights or the meaningfulness of the principles could be an area for further study.

Studies of motor learning have been concerned with task to task transfer, but the physical educator is also concerned with other kinds of transfer. Every student has heard the phrase, "Drills should be as game-like as possible." This precept certainly reflects the identical elements theory. The ability to transfer the performance of a skill to a game situation is extremely important. Further research is necessary to study this question.

Transfer of knowledge and strategy of games is also important. For example, in field hockey and soccer many elements are identical, and these should transfer positively. Many elements are similar but not identical; these elements may interfere with each other and result in negative transfer. For example, the names of the players and their positions are identical in the two games, elements which should transfer positively. However, the rules governing the position of the players following an out of bounds ball at the endline and the rule governing scoring are not the same and could result in negative transfer.

GENERALIZATIONS

1. Positive transfer may occur when two motor tasks have identical elements.

2. Positive transfer may occur when two tasks have the same perceptual components.

3. Skills involving similar patterns should not be taught at the same time.

BIBLIOGRAPHY

Bigge, Morris L., and Hunt, Maurice P. 1968. *Psychological Foundations of Education*. New York: Harper & Row, Publishers.

Broer, M. R. 1955. Evaluation of a basic skills curriculum for women students of low motor ability at the University of Washington. *Research Quarterly* 26:15.

———. 1958. Effectiveness of a general basic curriculum for junior high school girls. *Research Quarterly* 29:379.

Chui, Edward F. 1965. A study of golf-o-tron utilization as a teaching aid in relation to improvement and transfer. *Research Quarterly* 36:147.

Coleman, Dorothy. 1968. Effect of a unit of movement education upon the level of achievement in bowling. *Abstracts of Research Papers: AAHPER 1968 Convention*. Washington, D.C.: American Association for Health, Physical Education, and Recreation.

Colville, Frances. 1956. The learning of motor skills as influenced by a knowledge of general principles. Unpublished Ph.D. thesis, University of Southern California.

Cratty, Bryant J. 1962. Comparison of learning a fine motor task with learning a similar gross motor task using kinesthetic cues. *Research Quarterly* 33:212.

———. 1962. Transfer of small-pattern practice to large-pattern learning. *Research Quarterly* 33:523.

Cross, Thomas J. 1937. A comparison of the whole method, the minor game method, and the whole-part method of teaching basketball to ninth grade boys. *Research Quarterly* 8:49.

Harmon, John M., and Miller, Arthur G. 1950. Time patterns in motor learning. *Research Quarterly* 21:182.

Hause, Gerald W. 1944. A comparison of the progressive-part method and the whole method in teaching basketball shooting skills to high school boys. Unpublished Master's thesis, University of Alabama.

Judd, C. H. 1905. Movement and consciousness. *Psych. Rev.* 7:199.

Kimball, Edwin R. 1934. A comparative study of the whole and part methods of teaching basketball fundamentals. Unpublished Master's thesis, University of Southern California.

Knapp, Clyde, and Dixon, Robert. 1950. Learning to juggle. I: A study to determine the effect of two different distributions of practice on learning efficiency. *Research Quarterly* 21:331.

———. 1952. Learning to juggle. II: A study of whole and part methods. *Research Quarterly* 23:398.

Knapp, Clyde G.; Dixon, Robert W.; and Lazier, Murney. 1958. Learning to juggle. III: A study of performance by two different age groups. *Research Quarterly* 29:32.

Mohr, Dorothy R. 1960. The contributions of physical activity to skill learning. *Research Quarterly* 31:326.

Niemeyer, R. K. 1958. Part versus whole methods and massed versus distributed practice in learning of selected large muscle activities. Unpublished Ph.D. thesis, University of Southern California.

Nelson, Dale O. 1957. Studies of transfer of learning in gross motor skills. *Research Quarterly* 28:364.

Purdy, Bonnie J., and Stallard, Mary L. 1967. Effect of two learning methods and two grips on acquisition of power and accuracy in the golf swing of college women. *Research Quarterly* 38:480.

Riveness, Richard S. 1967. Multiple-task transfer effects in perceptual motor learning. *Research Quarterly* 38:485.

Ryan, E. Dean. 1965. Prerest and post rest performance on the stabilometer as a function of distribution of practice. *Research Quarterly* 36:197.

Scannell, Robert J. 1968. Transfer of accuracy training when difficulty is controlled by varying target size. *Research Quarterly* 39:341.

Singer, Robert N. 1965. Massed and distributed practice effects on the acquisition and retention of a novel basketball skill. *Research Quarterly* 36:68.

———. 1966. Transfer effects and ultimate success in archery due to degree of difficulty of the initial learning. *Research Quarterly* 37:532.

Skinner, B. F. 1957. *Science and Human Behavior*. New York: Appleton-Century-Crofts.

Stelmach, George. 1968. Effectiveness of motor learning as a function of the distribution of practice. *Abstracts of Research Papers: AAHPER 1968 Convention*. Washington, D.C.: American Association for Health, Physical Education, and Recreation.

Vincent, William J. 1968. Transfer effects between motor skills judged similar in perceptual components. *Research Quarterly* 39:380.

Wickstrom, Ralph L. 1958. Comparative study of methodologies for teaching gymnastics and tumbling stunts. *Research Quarterly* 29:10.

Young, Olive. 1954. Rate of learning in relation to spacing of practice periods in archery and badminton. *Research Quarterly* 25: 231.

6

Conceptualizing Techniques

The effects of conceptualizing techniques upon physical performance of gross motor skills has been a source of interest to many physical educators. The term *conceptualizing techniques* encompasses such terms used by investigators as mental practice and verbalization. *Mental practice* refers to a cognitive rehearsal of the skill. This can be accomplished through *imagery,* which means thinking about the movements necessary for performance or the accompanying sensations, or *directed* mental practice which involves directing the thinking of the performer through more specific instruction. *Verbalization* techniques further require the performer to describe movements or associated feelings through the spoken or written word.

Research design utilized in most studies of conceptualizing techniques include the use of one or more groups which practice conceptually, a physical practice group, and a control group which does not practice. Physical pre-tests and post-tests are usually given to all subjects and performance is analyzed to determine whether the groups have improved. In many cases differences between groups are tested for significance.

Problems in research include equalizing the

amount of time spent in physical and conceptual practice, and equalizing time within conceptual practice groups. Some investigators have conducted conceptual practice for a specific number of minutes while others have required a certain number of conceptual trials. Another research problem is controlling the conceptual practice of subjects outside of the practice time required in the investigation. In addition, it is impossible to know whether subjects are actually following directions for conceptual practice.

RELATED RESEARCH

The research related to conceptualizing techniques has been categorized under four major headings. "Imagery" includes studies in which this was the form of conceptual practice. "Directed mental practice" includes studies in which the investigators used written or spoken methods of directing the thinking of subjects. Studies in which performance resulting from mental practice was analyzed in terms of its relationship to verbal ability, intelligence, and kinesthesis are presented under the heading "relationship to other variables." "Preinstruction" is the heading for investigations in which this was a variable in the research design. When combinations of mental and physical practice were studied, they appear under the category "combined."

imagery

In a number of investigations, mental practice was described as imagining oneself performing the motor skill. Such imagery could be either visualization or kinesthetic sensation. Electromyographic studies by Jacobson (1932) revealed that imagining a movement results in potentials in the muscles involved in that movement.

Vandell, Davis, and Clugston (1953) ran a series of three studies with the same research design. Twelve subjects were divided into three groups. All groups performed the skill thirty-five times on the first and twentieth days of the experiment. Group one had no practice on the intervening days; group two practiced physically for thirty-five trials on each day; and group three practiced mentally for fifteen minutes daily. In the first study, senior high school boys were used as subjects and the skill was the basketball free throw. In the other studies the skill was dart throwing, with junior high school boys as subjects in the second and college freshmen as subjects in the third. The only statistical analysis was a measurement of the per cent of improvement for each group.

The analysis gave the following results: in the basketball free throw, the control group improved 2%, while the physical practice group improved 41% and the mental practice group 43%; in the junior high school dart throwing, the control group showed −2% improvement and the physical practice and mental practice groups showed 7% and 4% improvement respectively; finally, for the college freshmen in dart throwing, improvement was 0% for the control group, 23% for the physical practice group, and 22% for the mental practice group. Vandell concluded that mental practice was as effective as physical practice.

Twining (1949) used thirty-six college men as subjects and a ring toss as the motor task. All subjects received instruction and demonstration of the skill, followed by 210 tosses on the first day. On the twenty-second day of the experiment all subjects performed another 210 tosses. Per cent of improvement was the dependent variable tested for significance. Group one acted as the control group and had no practice on the intervening days. Group two had seventy ring tosses daily, and group three practiced mentally for fifteen minutes per day. Mental practice was defined as rehearsing the first day's activity. The control group showed an improvement of 4.3% which was not significant. The physical practice and mental practice groups showed significant improvements of 137.3% and 36.2% respectively. It was concluded that both physical practice and mental practice are effective in promoting learning.

Clarke (1960) conducted a study of 144 high school boys who practiced the one hand foul shot. The two treatment variables were physical practice and mental practice. Each group was composed of varsity players, junior varsity players, and novices. All subjects had the same instruction before the pre-test. They read about the techniques, had teacher instruction, and practiced mimetically. During twenty-five practice shots they received correction, and then were given a pre-test consisting of twenty-five shots. On each of the following fourteen days, the physical practice group had five warm up shots and twenty-five scored shots, while the mental practice group imagined five warm up shots and twenty-five scored shots.

Both groups showed a significant improvement. At the varsity level the physical practice group improved 16% and the mental practice group 15%. The junior varsity groups showed 24% improvement resulting from physical practice and 23% from mental practice. Novice groups improved 44% with physical practice and only 26% with mental practice. Mental practice and physical practice produced almost the same results for the varsity and junior varsity groups.

directed mental practice

Although all mental practice involves some kind of imagery, several investigators have attempted to further direct the mental practice of subjects by various techniques, such as reading descriptions of the skill, listening to descriptions of the skill, and verbalizing about the skill. Some investigators compared methods of directing practice, while others compared one or more methods of directing practice with physical practice or undirected mental practice.

Reading an instruction sheet related to the forward pass in football was the means of directing the mental practice of seventh grade boys in a study by Wills (1965). Sixty boys practiced the skill for three days and were placed into three equated groups on the basis of a thirty-trial pre-test. Then, on three days each week for five weeks, a physical practice group practiced five throws followed by thirty passes at a target. A mental practice group received an instruction sheet each day. Then they stood in position facing the target and thought through the practice schedule used by the physical practice group. A control group had no practice. A post-test of thirty trials was given to all three groups. The physical practice and mental practice groups improved significantly, whereas the control group did not. Comparisons among groups revealed that the mental practice group was significantly better than the control group.

Using three groups of ten high school boys and a wand juggling skill, Corbin (1967) studied the effects of physical and mental practice following physical practice. A control group practiced physically for five days and had no practice for the following thirteen days. The mental practice group heard directions for practice for thirteen days following five days of physical practice. The physical practice group practiced physically for eighteen days. Subjects were tested after the fifth and seventeenth days of practice. It was found that the control group did not improve; both the physical practice and mental practice groups improved significantly by the end of the study. The mean of the physical practice group was superior on both tests and the mean of the mental practice group was superior to that of the control group on the final test.

Johnson (1964) directed practice through the use of several verbalizing techniques. These techniques were combined with physical practice. Forty-six college women were divided into four groups. The task was a novel timed handball toss. Six trials of thirty seconds each were given to all subjects during each practice period. Group one had only physical practice. Group two had five minutes to write down answers to questions about the skill. Group three recorded verbal answers to the same questions on tape, using an interview technique. A fourth group thought through the answers to the same questions, and was further directed to imagine performance of the skill. All groups improved in performance after six days, although this improvement was not tested for significance. When the groups were compared, the physical practice group was significantly better than the written response group and the conceptualization group. There were no other differences between groups.

Several methods of directing practice were used by Whitehill (1964). Ninety-five fifth and sixth grade boys were divided into five groups. Five treatment variables were used: (1) a combination of demonstration and mental practice, (2) a combination of the use of diagrams and mental practice in which subjects studied the diagrams to get a mental image of the skill, (3) pure mental imagery, (4) a combination of kinesthetic and mental practice involving watching three demonstrations and rehearsing the skill mimetically, and (5) no practice of the skill. The skill was a one wall handball serve. Subjects practicing under the first three conditions improved significantly during eight practices of seven minutes duration. There were no differences between groups at the conclusion of the experiment.

Harby (1952) used film viewing as a means of mental practice. The motor task was the basketball free throw, practiced by 250 male college students. One group served as a control with no practice between the pre-test and post-test, each consisting of twenty trials. A physical practice group practiced twenty trials daily for twenty days. A mental practice group viewed a short film six times in a fifteen-

minute period for seven days. A second mental practice group viewed
the film for fourteen days. A third mental practice group viewed the
film for twenty days. A physical-mental practice group viewed the
film once daily, followed by twenty trials, for twenty days. A mental-
physical group viewed the film for fourteen days and practiced
physically for seven days. The physical practice group and fourteen-
day mental practice group improved significantly. The author suggested that there was an optimum length of time for mental practice.

Jones (1965) compared two methods of mental practice, using
seventy-one male college students as subjects. The task was a gymnastic hock wing upstart. Subjects practiced six times during a period
of two weeks. Instructions for practice included directed mental
practice for one group and undirected mental practice for the second
group. Both groups heard an analysis of the skill. Subjects were then
tested on the skill and those who failed the test were given further
mental practice followed by another skill test. The criterion was the
number of days required to pass the test.

On the first test fifty-six per cent of the subjects passed the test.
The undirected mental practice group had a signficantly higher per
cent of subjects passing the test than the directed mental practice
group. During subsequent testing and mental practice, the undirected
group was superior to the directed group.

relationship to other variables

A number of investigators have been interested in the relationship of intelligence, verbal ability, and kinesthesis to the ability to
practice mentally as measured by physical performance. Using the
underarm basketball free throw, Start (1960) had thirty-five eleven-
year-old boys practice mentally for five minutes during nine practice
periods. The practice consisted of having subjects picture themselves
performing the skill as it was verbally described to them. Subjects
had improved significantly when scores on a pre-test and post-test
were compared; but, though the improvement was significant, the
level of acquisition was quite low. On ten trials, the pre-test mean was
.77 and the post-test mean 1.46. The author pointed out that there
was no control group; therefore, it cannot be determined whether the
learning took place during the pre-test or during the mental practice
period. The subjects were divided into two groups on the basis of

intelligence: the high I. Q. group ranged from 106–117, the low
I. Q. group from 85–105. There were no significant differences between the gain scores of these groups. These findings were supported
by Clarke (1960), who found that intelligence had no influence
ability to practice mentally.

Johnson (1964) divided college women into two levels of
verbal ability on the basis of the college entrance exam. No differences
in the ability to use conceptualizing techniques could be related to
levels of verbal ability. Further findings showed a low relationship
between the abilities to verbalize and to perform.

Start (1964) studied the relationship between performance of
the single leg upstart on the Olympic high bar and a measure of
kinesthesis following a period of mental practice. Twenty-one male
college students were used as subjects. Six daily practice periods of
five minutes were devoted to reading a detailed analysis of the skill
and imagining performing the movements, listening to the reading of
the analysis while imagining performing, a combination of these
methods, imagery without the detailed analysis, and a final reading
of the analysis. Following the six practice periods, subjects were
rated on performance and given the Wiebe Test of Kinaesthesis. It
was found that kinesthesis had a very low correlation with performance of the skill which had been mentally practiced.

pre-instruction

The effects of several types of pre-instruction upon mental practice were compared by Surburg (1968), who used the tennis forehand drive as the motor skill. Subjects were 183 male college
students, assigned to seven groups. Two groups heard the audio ac-
companiment of a filmstrip. Two groups saw the filmstrip only, and
two groups saw the filmstrip and heard the audio recording. One of the
groups under each of these conditions also had a ten-minute mental
practice period during which members conceptualized the movements
involved in the tennis forehand drive. The seventh group was a control group. There were three practice sessions per week for eight
weeks. All mental practice groups showed a significant improvement,
and the audio-mental group was significantly better than the visual
and control groups. The author suggested that this group actually had
more mental practice than the others because they had to create their
own images of the skill.

physical-mental practice

Some investigators have included a comparison of combined physical and mental practice with physical or mental practice. Kelly (1965) placed 139 high school girls into five groups, using the overhand volleyball serve as the motor task. Treatment variables were assigned to the groups as follows: (1) imagery-mental practice, involving looking at photos of the skill and then imagining performance of twenty trials; (2) verbal-mental practice, which involved reading a verbal cue checklist and then imagining twenty trials; (3) physical practice, or the actual performance of twenty trials; (4) no practice, but a substitution of table tennis; and (5) physical-mental, which involved ten physical practice trials followed by ten imagery trials. Subjects practiced for ten days. The physical practice, physical-mental, and verbal-mental groups performed significantly better than the imagery-mental group.

Reeder (1968) had thirty-seven sixth grade girls practice a novel handball toss (see Figure 6.1) for five days under three different conditions. The first condition consisted of actual physical practice twenty times per day. The second was a combination of physical practice and mental practice, alternating five trials of each for a total of twenty trials per day. The mental practice involved imagery. The third condition was one of no practice. All groups improved significantly and there were no differences between groups.

Stebbins (1968) made random assignments of ninety-three male college students into five groups. Rubber balls were tossed at a target, and the score was the sum of the point values. The pre-test and post-test consisted of 100 trials with the dependent variable being the gain in score. There were eighteen practice sessions under five different conditions: (1) no practice; (2) mental practice, during which the subject stood beside someone physically practicing and mentally rehearsed twenty-five trials; (3) physical practice, or the actual performance of twenty-five trials; (4) mental-physical practice, consisting of mental practice for the first ten sessions and physical practice for the last eight sessions; and (5) physical-mental practice, a reverse of the mental-physical schedule. The combination methods were significantly better than the mental practice and the control. The physical practice group did not differ from any of the other groups,

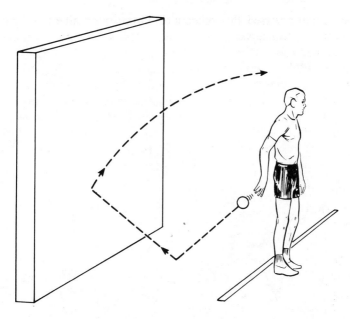

Figure 6.1 Novel Ball Toss

Represented photographically in Dava L. Reeder, "An Analysis of the Effect of Mental Practice as Combined with Physical Practice on Learning a Novel Gross Motor Skill" (Unpublished Paper, California State College at Los Angeles, 1968)

and the mental practice group did not show any improvement. The author suggested that this might have been due to the type of mental practice, as the person who was physically practicing could have been a distraction. The physical practice group improved significantly. The mental-physical practice group improved equally during both phases of practice. Both the mental-physical and physical-mental group improved significantly. There were no significant differences between these groups at the end of the first phase of the experiment.

Using a novel gross motor skill, Egstrom (1964) studied the effects of six conceptualizing schedules. The skill involved striking balls which were projected from a tube every twelve seconds, so as to hit a target. Subjects were 120 male college students randomly assigned to six groups. No differences were found between groups on a pre-test. Group one practiced physically for ten days. Group two practiced physically for five days and conceptualized for five days. A third group reversed this procedure. Group four alternated days of physical and conceptual practice, and a fifth group served as a control and had no practice. Conceptualizing practice included reading a description of the movements, mentally rehearsing the skill, and verbally describing the practice techniques into a tape recorder. Subjects were tested after the fifth and tenth days of practice. It was found that although conceptualizing practice was effective in acquiring the skill, physical practice was superior. Alternating the two types of practice resulted in performance equal to that resulting from physical practice.

DISCUSSION

It is generally accepted that the diver mentally rehearses a dive before its execution and that the golfer imagines his next shot while walking down the fairway. Investigations related to mental practice have attempted to assess the value of such practice scientifically.

Imagery is the form of mental practice utilized in most investigations. Subjects were directed to imagine themselves performing the skill. It is difficult to know whether such imagery consisted of visually picturing performance, or of imagining the kinesthetic feeling accompanying performance. Although in most investigations subjects physically performed the skill prior to mental practice, one might question whether they had enough successful experience to develop a kinesthetic feeling or memory which might be called upon later. It might be expected that more advanced performers would be better able to imagine kinesthetically.

Investigations involving imagery vary in terms of the skill employed, the age and sex of the subjects, and the amount of time spent in practice. Regardless of these variations, pure mental imagery did result in improved physical performance. Although physical practice groups employed in these studies also improved significantly, comparisons between groups were lacking.

In contrast to pure mental imagery, several investigators directed mental practice through the use of daily instruction sheets, verbalization techniques, and audio instruction. Although improvement was attributed to directed mental practice, comparisons with physical practice show conflicting results. In several investigations (Corbin, 1967; Egstrom, 1964; Kelly, 1965), physical practice was found to be superior to directed mental practice. The types of directed mental practice which were compared to physical practice included listening to directions for practice, writing answers to questions, thinking through answers to questions, reading a description of the movements, mentally rehearsing the skill, and verbally describing the practice techniques into a tape recorder. In other investigations (Johnson, 1964, and Wills, 1965), there were no differences in results between physical and mental practice. The types of mental practice included reading an instruction sheet and answering interview questions. When types of mental practice were compared, no differences were found between verbalization techniques (Johnson, 1964), demonstration and mental practice, diagrams and mental practice, pure mental imagery, and demonstration and mimetic practice (Whitehill, 1964). Furthermore, no consistent relationship emerged between the type of skill used, the amount of practice, age or sex of subjects, and the conflicting findings related to physical versus mental practice. In one study (Jones, 1965), undirected mental practice was found to be superior to directed mental practice; but this finding is contradicted by the findings of two other investigations (Kelly, 1965, and White-hill, 1964). More research is needed to clarify these issues.

The physical educator must be concerned with the place of mental practice in the class setting. Because of class size and organization, all students cannot practice physically at the same time. Perhaps better use of class time could include having students practice mentally while waiting for their turn to practice physically. However, when mental practice consisted of watching someone perform physically (Stebbins, 1968), there was no improvement. This finding would suggest that if students practice mentally while waiting their turn, they should be cautioned not to watch the person performing or they should use a form of directed mental practice which turns their attention away from the person practicing.

Studies related to combinations of mental and physical practice indicate that this procedure may be better than mental practice by itself. The combinations used by investigators are quite varied. One investigator (Kelly, 1965) found that a daily combination of ten physical trials followed by ten imagery trials was superior to pure mental practice. Other effective combinations involved schedules of a number of physical or mental practice days followed by a number of days of the reverse (Stebbins, 1968), or alternating mental and physical practice days (Egstrom, 1964). Because physical practice is also considered necessary for the sake of exercise, a combination of physical and mental practice within a single class period appears most desirable for physical education classes.

There are many variations in the amount of time allowed for mental practice and physical practice. Time for mental practice ranged from fifteen minutes (Vandell, Davis and Chegston, 1953) to five minutes (Egstrom, 1964). When subjects practiced mentally for a number of trials, it is not always clear whether all subjects took the same length of time or whether their practice time equaled that of physical practice groups. The number of days of practice also varies considerably in the investigations related to mental practice. One investigator (Harby, 1952) suggested that there might be an optimum amount of time for mental practice. Further research is necessary to investigate this problem.

It is possible that advanced performers would be better able to profit from mental practice than beginners. No studies have been designed to compare such groups of subjects. Corbin (1967) suggested that previous practice of a skill is necessary before mental practice, although he did not designate a specific necessary level of skill. In comparing physical practice with mental practice, Clarke (1960) found them equally effective for varsity and junior varsity players, whereas novices appeared to benefit more from physical practice. These findings were not statistically treated, but they offer a suggestion for further research.

Interestingly, most of the skills used in research have involved a projectile. This raises the question of whether mental practice would improve performance in other types of activities, such as swimming, dance, tumbling, and gymnastics. In the two studies using gymnastics, the research emphasis was not on the amount of improvement which could be attributed to mental practice, but on a comparison between two methods of practicing mentally in one case (Jones, 1965) and on the relationship between mental practice and kinesthesis in the other case (Start, 1964).

In spite of the large amount of research on mental practice, the physical educator is faced with more unanswered than answered questions. Those which remain unanswered concern the effectiveness of mental versus physical practice, the most effective means of directing mental practice, the optimum amount of time for practice, and the relationship of skill level, age, and sex to the ability to practice mentally. At present, only three generalizations appear to be supported by research findings: mental practice improves performance and is unrelated to intelligence, verbal ability, and kinesthesis; physical practice is as effective as or more effective than conceptual practice; mental practice results in improved physical performance.

GENERALIZATIONS

1. There is no apparent relationship between intelligence or verbal ability and the effect of mental practice.
2. Performance in motor skills can be improved through directed or undirected mental practice.
3. Physical practice results in performance equal to or better than performance resulting from conceptual practice.

BIBLIOGRAPHY

Clarke, L. Verdelle. 1960. Effect of mental practice on the development of a certain motor skill. *Research Quarterly* 31:560.

Corbin, Charles B. 1967. Effects of mental practice on skill development after controlled practice. *Research Quarterly* 38:534.

Egstrom, Glen H. 1964. Effects of an emphasis on conceptualizing techniques during early learning of a gross motor skill. *Research Quarterly* 35:472.

Harby, S. F. 1952. *Comparison of mental practice and physical practice in the learning of physical skills.* (SDC 269-7-27) Special Devices Center, Office of Naval Research.

Jacobson, Edmond. 1932. Electrophysiology of mental activities. *Am. J. Psych.* 44:677.

Johnson, Joan D. 1964. The effect of selected conceptualizing techniques upon the early learning of a gross movement. Unpublished Ph.D. thesis, University of Southern California.

Jones, John G. 1965. Motor learning without demonstration of physical practice, under two conditions of mental practice. *Research Quarterly* 36:270.

Kelly, Darlene A. 1965. The relative effectiveness of selected mental practice techniques in high school girls' acquisition of a gross motor skill. Unpublished Master's thesis, University of Washington.

Reeder, Dava L. 1968. An analysis of the effect of mental practice as combined with physical practice on learning a novel gross motor skill. Unpublished paper, California State College at Los Angeles.

Start, K. B. 1960. Relationship between intelligence and the effect of mental practice on the performance of a motor skill. *Research Quarterly* 31:644.

————. 1964. Kinaesthesis and mental practice. *Research Quarterly* 35:316.

Stebbins, Richard J. 1968. A comparison of the effects of physical and mental practice in learning a motor skill. *Research Quarterly* 39:714.

Surburg, Paul R. 1968. Audio, visual, and audio-visual instruction with mental practice in developing the forehand tennis drive. *Research Quarterly* 39:728.

Twining, W. E. 1949. Mental practice and physical practice in learning a motor skill. *Research Quarterly* 20:432.

Vandell, Roland A.; Davis, R. A.; and Clugston, H. A. 1953. The function of mental practice in the acquisition of motor skills. *J. General Psychol.* 29:243.

Whitehill, M. Patrick. 1964. A comparison of different variations of mental practice on the ability of boys to learn a motor skill. Unpublished Master's thesis, University of Oregon.

Wills, Keith C. 1965. The effect of mental practice and physical practice on learning a motor skill. Unpublished Master's thesis, Arkansas State College.

7

Retention

Information about levels of performance following the original learning of a skill and a period without practice of that skill is important to the physical educator in program planning. Investigators have sought to discover what levels of performance can be expected after varying periods of no practice, and which factors are significant in producing the highest levels of performance following periods of no practice.

An important problem in such research is the loss of subjects during the no-practice period. Longer intervals usually mean a greater loss of subjects. Such losses may create a final test group which represents only those subjects who were most interested during the original learning period or those who come from homes where the parent's occupation causes residential permanence. Other factors could influence the findings of the study and, therefore, the extent to which these findings can be generalized. Controlling the no-practice period is another research problem. It is important that subjects do not practice the task either physically or mentally, but mental practice cannot be controlled. Investigators have often used novel skills rather than actual skills found in physical education activities in an attempt to control physical practice. It is just as important that subjects do not practice a task with either positive or negative transfer during the no-practice period.

Performance following no-practice periods has been measured in several ways. *Retention* refers to the level of performance following periods of no practice; thus, retention measurements indicate the amount remembered. Retention has been measured after periods of minutes, hours, days, weeks, months, and years. Retention measurements are generally reported in one of two ways. *Absolute* retention measurements are actual comparisons of scores. *Relative* retention measurements reflect the per cent of original learning retained. The type of measurement can seriously affect the findings of an investigation. For example, subjects were tested on ten trials of a motor task which was practiced under three different original learning conditions. Results are shown in Table 1. Group I showed the highest mean

TABLE 1
Absolute and Relative Retention Measures

Group	Original learning performance scores	Absolute retention performance scores	Relative retention (per cent)
I	8	7	88
II	5	4	80
III	4	4	100

score during original learning, and group III the lowest. Relative retention measurements indicate that group III retained 100% of its original performance whereas group I retained only 88%. This might suggest that the practice method used by group III during original learning is better than the other methods. When absolute retention measurements are compared, however, it can be seen that the actual performance of group I following the no-practice period was superior to that of the other two groups. This suggests that the method of practice used by group I yields the highest levels of performance and thus is the best method. Relative retention measures give a good indication of the amount retained; absolute retention measures reflect the level of performance.

Relearning is often studied in relation to retention. It is measured as the amount of practice necessary to reach original levels of performance following a period of no practice. Findings have implications for physical education program planning in terms of the amount of time necessary for review.

Reminiscence is another term found in the literature related to retention. This word refers to an increase in levels of performance following periods of no practice. Most investigators have observed reminiscence, though few have tested the change in performance for significance. When reminiscence occurs, the reason for the increase should be carefully studied. It is possible that subjects are still learning when they take retention tests or that maturation or growth accounts for the increase in performance.

Investigators in fields other than physical education have reported that retention is highest when a task has been overlearned. *Overlearning* means that practice of the skill is continued after a certain level of performance has been reached. Due to the complexity of the tasks used in physical education, it is doubtful that overlearning occurs during the time span of an investigation. Tasks which many people have overlearned, however, might be exemplified by bicycle riding and driving a car.

RELATED RESEARCH

The investigations of retention that have used tasks similar to those found in physical education activities may be divided into three categories: studies concerned with the amount retained, with the effect of the nature of the task upon retention, and with the effect of the original learning conditions upon retention.

amount of retention

Several investigations have studied the subjects' amounts of retention following no-practice periods of minutes, days, weeks, and months. A juggling task was used in one of the earliest studies (Swift, 1906). After one year of no practice, two subjects were retested, and though retention measures were low, relearning occurred rapidly. One subject was tested six years later with similar findings.

After one year of no practice, Purdy and Lockhart (1962) retested thirty-six college women who had been classified into high, average, and low skill groups on the basis of original learning. Five novel gross motor skills were used: a nickel toss, ball toss, foot volley, lacrosse throw and catch, and a bongo board balance. Subjects practiced for three days and scores were averaged as the measure of relearning. It was found that the total group retained 94% of its original learning. Original levels of performance were elicited. In both retention and relearning, subjects remained in the skill groups into which they were originally classified.

Ryan (1965) studied the retention and relearning of performance on a stabilometer, using subjects from 22 to 27 years of age. Original learning took place during eleven thirty-second trials. Thirty subjects were placed in each of three groups on the basis of original learning, and were retested after three, six, or twelve months of no practice. The three-month and six-month groups lost 40% and 58% of original performance respectively, whereas the twelve-month group lost 81%. There were no significant differences in the amount lost by the three-month and six-month groups; however, the twelve-month group lost significantly more than the six-month group. On a second trial on the stabilometer, there were no significant differences between groups. The three-month and six-month groups relearned to the original level of performance by the fourth trial, and the twelve-month group by the eighth trial. When subjects were classified as "good performers" and "poor performers" on the basis of original learning, there were no significant differences in the amount of change between these groups following the no-practice periods. The author explained that the differences between the findings of this study and the Purdy-Lockhart study (1962) concerning the amount retained were due to the method of measuring retention. Had similar measurements been used, Ryan's results would have indicated that the three-month and six-month groups retained 98% of their best performance, and the twelve-month group 83%.

The Bachman ladder climb was used by Meyers (1967) in a retention study involving ten minutes, one day, one week, four weeks, and thirteen weeks of no practice. One hundred senior high school girls were divided into five groups. Original learning consisted of ten thirty-second trials with sixty-second rest intervals. There were no significant losses in performance following the no-practice period for any of the groups.

Bell conducted two studies involving twenty trials per day for ten days over a five-week period. The task used in the first study was the badminton long serve (1966), and for the second study (1968) a novel handball toss was designed. Subjects were given twenty trials following five weeks of no practice. When absolute retention was compared with performance on the tenth practice day of the original learning period, there were no significant changes in performance.

nature of the task

Investigations of retention have included a study of the effect of type of task upon retention. Investigators have attempted to determine whether certain types of tasks are retained more readily than others.

Naylor and Briggs (1961) suggest that meaningful materials, whether verbal or motor, are retained better than nonsense or unorganized sequences of material.

Investigations using tracking tasks and procedural tasks have suggested that continuous tasks in which adjustments are made to a changing stimulus are retained better than discrete tasks in which a distinct response is required. It is difficult to classify gross motor skills into these categories. Such things as bicycle riding and swimming possibly represent continuous tasks, and throwing or striking movements represent discrete tasks. However, when physical educators have studied the nature of the task in relation to retention and relearning, skills have not been classified as continuous or discrete.

Purdy and Lockhart (1962) found no differences in retention of five motor skills following one year of no practice. A balance skill was relearned significantly better than a nickel toss, foot volley, lacrosse throw and catch, and a ball toss.

When groups receiving twenty, thirty, and forty trials of original learning were compared on relearning, Purdy (1964) found that the forty-trial group performed a lacrosse throw and catch and a balancing skill significantly better than the other two groups. Other skills used in the study were a stylus maze for time and errors and a foot volley. There were no significant differences between groups on the number of relearning trials necessary to reach initial levels of performance on the five skills.

Using a relative retention measure, the balance skill was the least well retained. Although the forty-trial group was superior to the other groups in the balance and lacrosse skills, and the twenty-trial group was superior in the foot volley in initial learning, this difference between groups did not exist when absolute retention scores were compared.

original learning conditions

Conditions which affect original learning have been discussed in other chapters. Few investigators have compared performance measures following no-practice periods to determine whether differences in retention might be due to certain original learning conditions. The learning conditions which have been studied in relation to retention include the amount of original practice, feedback available during original learning, and massed versus distributed practice sessions.

Amount of original practice. Purdy (1964) conducted an investigation designed to study the effects of the number of practice trials upon retention and relearning. Ninety college women were randomly assigned to three groups. Skills utilized were a stylus maze, balance board, lacrosse throw and catch against a wall, and a foot volley. Performance was measured in each of the skills as follows:

1. Stylus maze: number of errors
2. Stylus maze: time
3. Balance board: number of errors in fifteen seconds
4. Lacrosse throw and catch: number of catches in fifteen seconds
5. Foot volley: number of consecutive volleys

Following an initial unscored practice period, the three groups received initial practice periods of twenty, thirty, or forty trials for each skill. When standard scores on the first five trials for each skill were added and compared, it was found that the groups did not differ significantly. When standard scores for the last five trials for each skill were added and compared, it was found that the forty-trial group had significantly higher scores than the other groups, and that there were no significant differences between the twenty-trial and thirty-trial groups.

A relative retention measure consisted of one trial following 26–30 days of no practice. Measures on the five skills revealed that the twenty-trial group retained 87% of its performance on the last practice trial, the thirty-trial group 80%, and the forty-trial group

63%. When absolute retention measures were compared, no significant differences were found among the groups. The number of trials necessary to relearn to original levels of performance were also compared and no significant differences were found. A mean of 3.10 trials was required by the total group to reach the final performance level. A mean of 6.90 trials was required to reach this level on two relearning days. Reminiscence was noted on the maze time for the twenty-trial group and on maze error for the twenty-trial and thirty-trial groups.

Feedback during practice. Bell (1966) found that college students who practiced the badminton long serve under four different conditions employing augmented knowledge of results showed no differences in absolute retention after five weeks of no practice. In a second study (1968), groups practicing a novel handball toss with visual or verbal knowledge of results displayed no differences in absolute retention after five weeks of no practice. It was suggested that sufficient knowledge of results was inherent in the tasks, and that the knowledge of results supplied by the investigator did not affect the retention of the motor skills.

Massed vs. distributed practice. Using a novel skill in which subjects bounced a basketball from the floor into the basket under massed and distributed practice conditions, Singer (1965) found that the group having eighty massed practice trials displayed significant reminiscence when tested one month later. In addition, this group and the group having eighty trials with five-minute rest periods between every twenty trials retained significantly more after one month than the group having eighty trials with a twenty-four hour rest between every twenty trials.

DISCUSSION

Information concerning retention and relearning of gross motor skills is of paramount importance to the physical educator in program planning. In many instances the practice of a motor skill is interrupted. Such interruptions consist of the time between class meetings, weekends, vacations, and the repetition of a unit in a particular activity. The physical educator needs to know what effect such interruptions have upon the performance of motor skills. This information provides a basis for planning lessons around interruptions of varying lengths of time.

The investigations presented in this chapter indicate that original levels of performance on several types of gross motor skills are retained over no-practice periods of days, weeks, and months. The nature of the task does not appear to influence the amount retained.

Relative retention measures indicate that a high per cent of original performance is retained. This might suggest that little time need be devoted to review and relearning of motor skills following no-practice periods. However, evaluation of the absolute measurement of original levels of performance might alter this point of view. For example, in evaluating the original level of performance following practice, Bell (1968) found that although subjects improved significantly and retained what they had learned, a significant improvement did not necessarily indicate a high level of original performance. When the badminton long serve and a ball toss were practiced twenty times daily for ten days, a total of 200 trials, performance on the tenth day was approximately 25% of that which might have been achieved. Mean scores were less than five correct responses out of a possible twenty. Although this level of performance was retained following five weeks of no practice, it cannot be assumed that high levels of performance appeared on the retention test. The complexity of a projectile gross motor skill appears to be an important factor in evaluating the findings of retention and relearning studies. Following a line drawing study, Baker and Young (1960) suggested that there were two phases of learning. They hypothesized that during phase one, the learner corrected his constant error, and that although he improved during phase two, retention returned to the level of performance acquired during phase one. They further suggested that phase one of learning took place on the first day of line drawing practice. At this time, the poorest group achieved approximately 25% of that which they might have achieved, and the best group achieved approximately 40%. During phase two, the poorest group showed an increase of approximately 15% in level of performance, and the best group showed an increase of approximately 20%. When these levels of performance are compared with those achieved in the badminton long serve and the handball toss, it seems possible that subjects performing the more complex motor skills had not advanced to the second learning phase at the conclusion of the practice period. This would explain why the level of acquisition was equal to the level of retention. If practice in the more complex task were continued over a longer period of time, the results of retention measurements might indicate findings more like those of investigations using simple motor skills. However, the practicality of a substantially longer period of practice within a physical education activity unit is doubtful.

In planning the amount of original practice, it must also be remembered that Purdy (1964) found no differences in absolute retention between groups practicing twenty, thirty, or forty trials, although relative retention was high. She further suggested that the original level of performance was the important factor in determining the amount retained. This suggestion was further substantiated by Purdy and Lockhart (1962), who found that subjects remained at the same skill level into which they were originally classified. These findings substantiate the need for developing practice situations which will yield the highest levels of original performance within a unit of a physical education activity.

The physical educator must ask himself how much practice and what kind of practice in subsequent classes will raise the level of performance which has been retained. The answer to that question can only be found through a series of long term studies. Retention studies to date have only involved beginning levels of performance, but it would be desirable to follow groups of subjects through other stages of learning over a period of years. The point at which over-learning begins might thus be identified.

The need for progression in developing complex motor skills becomes apparent. Although beginners have been the subjects of investigations, measurement of skill has been based on ultimate performance. In other words, there have been no intermediate goals. The beginner's performance has been measured in the same terms as one might measure the advanced person's performance. Perhaps physical educators should make a careful analysis of motor skills, requiring less of the beginner and progressively refining the goals. Performance measures at each level of learning might then show higher levels of performance. In this way, assuming that students retain what they have learned or will relearn quickly, the teacher would have a basis for the establishment of new goals and more complex practice situations involving the same skill.

Retention investigations have involved the use of isolated skills as treatment variables. In physical education activities, however, the combination of skills into a meaningful whole includes knowledge, understanding, and use of skills, rules, and strategy. At this point, the only insight for physical educators concerning retention of these factors is the suggestion supplied by Naylor and Briggs (1961) that organized and meaningful materials are better retained than unorganized materials. In planning lessons, therefore, the educated judgment of the teacher must be employed to present materials in a meaningful way.

GENERALIZATIONS

1. Motor skills are retained over no-practice periods of days, weeks, and months.
2. Motor skills are relearned to a certain level of performance in a shorter period of time than was necessary to reach the same level during original learning.
3. The nature of the task does not appear to influence the amount retained.
4. The level of original learning is more indicative of the level of performance on retention than the number of original practice trials.
5. Varying methods of providing the learner with knowledge of results does not appear to affect retention.

BIBLIOGRAPHY

Baker, C. H., and Young, Phyllis. 1960. Feedback during training and retention of motor skills. *Canad. J. Psychol.* 14:257–64.

Bell, V. L. 1966. Augmented knowledge of results related to constant and variable errors and its effect upon acquisition and retention of a gross motor skill. Unpublished Ph.D. thesis, University of Southern California.

————. 1968. Visual and verbal feedback and its effect upon acquisition and retention of a projectile skill. Unpublished study, California State College at Los Angeles.

Meyers, J. L. 1967. Retention of balance coordination learning as influenced by extended lay-offs. *Research Quarterly* 38:72–78.

Naylor, J. C., and Briggs, G. E. 1961. *Long term retention of learned skills; a review of the literature.* ASD Technical Report 61-340. Washington, D.C.: U.S. Dept. of Commerce.

Purdy, B. J. 1964. Effect of number of practice trials in initial learning on retention and relearning of motor skills. Unpublished Ph.D. thesis, University of Southern California.

Purdy, B. J., and Lockhart, A. 1962. Retention and relearning of gross motor skills after long periods of no practice. *Research Quarterly* 33:194–220.

Ryan, E. Dean. 1965. Retention of stabilometer performance over extended periods of time. *Research Quarterly* 36:46–51.

Singer, R. N. 1965. Massed and distributed practice effects on the acquisition and retention of a novel basketball skill. *Research Quarterly* 36:68–77.

Swift, E. J. 1906. Memory of skillful movements. *Psychol. Bull.* 3: 185–87.

part four
APPLICATIONS AND IMPLICATIONS

Chapter 8 provides a synthesis of what is now known about motor learning. Suggestions are made concerning the use of this knowledge in planning a unit in physical education as well as in planning a lesson. Research techniques applicable to the classroom are also presented.

8

Program Planning

The generalizations presented in this book are designed to help develop meaningful guides for program planning. They are an attempt to synthesize research findings to date, to suggest avenues for study, and to guide the physical educator in planning learning experiences. The generalizations can be used as guides for the planning of individual lessons and of larger blocks of time or units in an activity. The findings of individual investigations, in which the nature of the activity appears to interact with the conditions under study, may also serve as guides to program planning. This chapter is divided into four sections: the first section is a synthesis of research findings in specific physical education activities; the second section contains suggestions for consideration in planning an activity unit; the third offers suggestions for planning individual lessons; and the fourth presents an outline for conducting classroom research.

ACTIVITIES

The generalizations so far presented in this book have been derived from research on general topics such as communication, knowledge of results, methods of practice, and retention. It is also possible to synthesize research findings in terms of physical education activities, as in this chapter. When this is done it is surprising to note how little research has been conducted in each activity.

archery

Massed practice, four days per week was superior to distributed practice, two days per week (Young, 1954). When difficulty level was defined in terms of distance, there were no differences between transferring from shorter to longer distances and transferring from longer to shorter distances (Singer, 1966).

badminton

When badminton was used as the motor task, there were no differences between groups taught with and without the use of film-strips, slow motion loop films, or loop films (Feinberg, 1951; Gray and Brumbach, 1967; Nelson, 1958). There were no differences on performance measures between groups taught with and without the use of mechanical principles (Mikesell, 1962); however, when scores on knowledge and skill tests were combined, students receiving instruction in mechanical principles were superior to those who had no such instruction (Broer, 1955). Practice interrupted by a day of rest was superior to practice on successive days (Young, 1954). During early learning, distributed practice for thirty minutes per day three times a week was superior to massed practice for sixty minutes per day twice a week (Niemeyer, 1958). During later learning, the game method of practice resulted in better performance on skills than a part method of practicing individual skills (Niemeyer, 1958). Performance on the long serve was retained following five weeks of no practice (Bell, 1966). Varying methods of providing the learner with knowledge of results during the practice of the long serve resulted in the same level of performance for all groups (Bell, 1966).

basketball

When a part was defined as a total skill, the part method was better than the game method of practicing skills (Kimball, 1934). A group receiving a unit in mechanical principles performed as well as or better than a group receiving no such unit (Broer, 1958). Mental practice consisting of imagery resulted in a significant improvement on the foul shot (Clarke, 1960). Mental practice directed through viewing a film resulted in a significant improvement in the basketball free throw (Harby, 1952).

baseball

Knowledge of results concerning both speed and accuracy resulted in the best performance on these factors in the baseball throw (Malina, 1963). Viewing motion pictures of batting faults decreased the number of such faults (Watkins, 1963).

bowling

Motion picture demonstration was valuable in teaching bowling after the subjects had had some practice (Lockhart, 1944).

football

Teaching recognition of football plays through motion pictures was superior to a flash card method (Londeree, 1967). Reading an instruction sheet which directed mental practice of the football pass resulted in a significant improvement in performance (Wills, 1965).

golf

When a whole was defined as a total swing, the whole method of practice was superior to the part method of practicing the golf swing (Purdy and Stallard, 1967). Practice with the 7-iron transferred positively to the 4-iron (Chui, 1965).

gymnastics

Instant videotape replay resulted in better performance on skills than teaching without this means of providing knowledge of results (Plese, 1968). Undirected mental practice was superior to a directed method of mental practice in a gymnastic skill (Jones, 1965). There were no differences between a whole method of practicing gymnastic skills and a whole-direct-repetitive (progressive part) method of practice (Wickstrom, 1958).

softball

Previous instruction in mechanical principles resulted in equal or better performance on skills, compared with that of a group receiving no such instruction (Broer, 1958).

swimming

The whole method of teaching swimming skills resulted in better performance than a part method in which the elements of the skill were taught separately (Niemeyer, 1958). Instruction in mechanical principles resulted in performance equal to or better than that of groups receiving no such instruction (Garland, 1960, and Mohr and Barrett, 1962).

tennis

Equal emphasis on speed and accuracy produced the best results in learning the tennis forehand drive (Woods, 1967). Knowledge of results consisting of performance scores had no effect on learning tennis (Johnson, 1961). Mental practice involving the use of the audio portion of a filmstrip was superior to mental practice involving the use of the video portion of the filmstrip (Surburg, 1968).

tumbling

No differences appeared between groups when one group was shown motion pictures of experts and of their own performance and the other group received no such visual communication (Brown and Messersmith, 1948).

volleyball

A unit in mechanical principles before teaching volleyball resulted in performance on skills which was equal to or better than that of a group not having the previous instruction (Broer, 1958). When a part was defined as a total skill, the part method of practicing skills resulted in better performance than a game method (Niemeyer, 1958). A physical practice group, a physical-mental practice group, and a verbal mental practice group performed the overhand volleyball serve better than an imagery mental practice group (Kelly, 1965). During later learning, massed practice for ninety minutes per day twice a week was superior to distributed practice for sixty minutes per day three days a week (Niemeyer, 1958).

PLANNING THE UNIT

Research findings concerning the learning of gross motor skills provide a basis for some suggestions about planning a unit in a physical education class. Some of the factors the teacher should consider are related to retention, transfer, motivation, and methods of practice.

The past experience of the students should be considered in planning the unit. If students have had previous experience in the activity, it may be expected that the motor skills will be retained or relearned quickly. Little time need be spent on review in order to achieve original levels of performance. Further practice may be necessary, however, to increase the original level of performance. Records should be kept of students' performance on skills tests. These will provide a basis for evaluating original levels of performance and will serve as guides in planning subsequent units in the same activity.

Opportunities for transfer should be considered in planning the unit. When students have had previous experience in physical education activities whose elements are identical to those involved in the activities in the unit being planned, positive transfer might be expected. Generalizations such as those derived from mechanical principles might also be expected to transfer if the teacher can evoke the students' insight and desire to make such transfer. The unit should include opportunities to develop understandings related to mechanical principles for possible transfer to subsequent situations. In addition to transfer from one unit to another, possibilities for transfer within a unit should be anticipated. In learning new skills within the same unit, previous experience with identical elements or generalizations provides an opportunity for positive transfer. If positive transfer is anticipated, the learning periods of succeeding skills may be shortened.

The students should be motivated to learn, and the importance of motivation has a neurological basis. If the learner is motivated, he will perceive more sensory information. Although there is little evidence concerning the use of motivating devices in physical education activities, it appears that since varied methods of providing sensory input have the same effect upon performance, varied approaches to individual lessons within a unit may lessen the chances of boredom and thus have a motivating effect. For example, the form of a skill may be presented through live demonstration in one instance and through the use of a film or other visual aid in another instance. The type of knowledge of results provided following performance is another possibility for variation.

The teacher should plan the means of practicing the skills included in the unit. Provision should be made for the isolated practice of skills before they are practiced in a game situation. In planning the distribution of practice throughout the unit, the teacher should refer to individual studies of massed and distributed practice, since the nature of the activity apparently interacts with the type of practice. In any event, the practice of a skill should be distributed over a period of days to increase levels of performance.

The teacher should consider the factors important in yielding retention. If he wishes to provide opportunities for overlearning, the unit might be structured to include practicing a few skills over a period of days, rather than introducing as many skills as possible within the unit. The teacher should strive to develop lessons which will yield high levels of original learning in order to achieve high levels of retention.

PLANNING THE LESSON

One of the first steps in lesson planning is to determine what information should be communicated to the learner and how it should be communicated. If the form of a new skill is to be communicated, the teacher has several choices. He may use live demonstration, moving pictures, film strips, or loop films with equal success. It is also important that the student understand what is expected of him. In a projectile skill he should understand the desired trajectory of the projectile and the degree of accuracy required. The teacher may communicate these factors verbally or through a visual aid. In addition, the teacher may wish to include the mechanical principles applicable to the performance of the skill. Knowledge of mechanical principles may increase learning.

In teaching a new skill the whole skill should be presented and practiced. If both speed and accuracy are required, as in a projectile skill, they should both be practiced. Although little is known about massed and distributed practice, it appears that practice should continue over a period of days, rather than being massed and practiced in a single class period. Large class size and lack of equipment usually make rest intervals necessary between trials. During this time students may be encouraged to practice mentally; they should be instructed to practice without watching the students who are practicing physically.

Attention should be given to providing the learner with knowledge of results. The use of motion pictures or video tapes of students' performance may assist in the correction of movement errors. Projectile skills contain considerable inherent information which may be of value to the learner. Augmenting that information does not alter performance; therefore, practice situations may be structured in different ways.

The following lesson plan was developed and justified with generalizations drawn from the literature. It serves as an example of the use of what is now known about motor learning in a teaching situation.

Sample Plan for Badminton, Lesson 2

Content	Procedures	Justification
1. Roll call	1. By court area	
2. Forehand grip	2. "Shake hands with racket," demonstrate, have the class copy example. Emphasize that wrist must be easy to maneuver and one should be able to hear "swishing" sound	2. Cues inherent in the task aid in retention. Demonstration facilitates learning of a task in its initial stages. Knowledge of results, as from the racket "swish," aids

Sample Plan for Badminton, Lesson 2 (Cont.)

Content	Procedures	Justification
	when racket is swung. Class tries grip and swings until they hear loud sound. Check each person; be sure they realize that the wrist will aid in giving force to the projection.	in learning. Finally, in all probability, a knowledge of mechanical principles, as in using the wrist along with the arm for more force, will aid in learning.
3. Ready position	3. Have class copy demonstration of correct positioning. Emphasize its principles and how they will aid in movement on the court.	3. Demonstration facilitates learning in its initial stages. A knowledge of mechanical principles may improve performance.
4. Footwork	4. Shots to the right of player should be received with the left foot forward, knees bent. Demonstrate with class copying. Take class back to ready position each time.	4. Demonstration aids in the learning of a task. Improved performance is a function of the amount of proper practice trials. By taking the class back to the ready position, their original learning is reinforced.
5. Holding shuttle	5. Demonstrate easiest method, position of arm and body. Relate to footwork. Practice dropping bird in front of body to prescribed spot on floor.	5. Demonstration aids in the learning of a task in its initial stages. Visual results, given by letting the shuttle drop, are necessary for improvement and hasten learning.
6. Starting the bird	6. Relate to bowling, softball pitch, or any underhand pattern. Demonstrate the stroke and tell the class what the	6. Identical elements transfer. Practice the whole skill. Demonstration facilitates learning in its initial

Content	Procedures	Justification
	bird should do. Have them go through the stroke, following movements of instructor. Emphasize critical points in stroke such as the wrist snap, weight transfer. Assign to courts with the extra students working on position, footwork, wrist action, and dropping the bird. Instructor goes to each court to give individual instruction. Class told not to return the bird, but to let it drop to see where it lands. Rotate extra players with those on the courts.	stages. Acquisition of a skill is better with feedback, given by letting the bird drop after hitting it.

Note: Reprinted by permission of the author from "Badminton Unit Plan," by Sue Harris (unpublished paper, California State College, Los Angeles, 1968).

CLASSROOM RESEARCH: DESIGN

The generalizations which have been drawn from research in motor learning should be utilized with the understanding that they are by no means conclusive. Strictly speaking, conclusions drawn from investigations may only be applied with confidence under conditions exactly like the conditions of the investigation. For example, most motor learning experiments have not been carried out in the classroom situation, and they have used subjects of a specific age, sex, and skill level. These conditions are not exactly like the ones encountered in each teaching situation. The teacher may find it desirable to conduct classroom research to support or refute the use of generalizations drawn from other situations as a further guide to program planning. A hypothetical study will be used here to present the procedures which may be followed in conducting classroom research.

the problem

The problem or purpose of a study should be clearly stated and limited. A clear statement is a directive in designing the procedure to be used in solving the problem. An unclear statement is ambiguous and of little value as a directive.

Unclear: The purpose of the study was to investigate the effects of mental practice.

Clear: The purpose of the study was to investigate the effectiveness of (1) mental imagery and (2) physical practice in the learning of a gross motor skill. Specifically, the problem was to compare the effectiveness of five minutes of mental imagery with five minutes of physical practice five days per week for two weeks in the acquisition of the basketball free throw.

The clear statement reflects thinking which includes a definition of the type of mental practice, what it will be compared with, how long the practice will be, and what specific skill will be used.

The study should be limited to a specific age, skill level, and sex. For example:

This study was limited to seventh grade girls enrolled in two beginning basketball classes at Lincoln Junior High School, City, State.

selection of subjects

In classroom research the teacher uses the subjects available to him. The students enrolled in the class become the subjects for the investigation. The ideal way to obtain two like groups of subjects is to select randomly from the total student population and to assign those subjects who were selected to two classes. More often, however, the teacher must use two intact classes. In other words, he uses two classes selected on the basis of the school's registration procedures. It is important that the two classes contain subjects who have the same characteristics such as age, sex, skill level, intelligence, and other known variables. It is desirable to give both groups a pre-test to determine whether they differ significantly before the investigation. If they do not differ on the pre-test and are alike in terms of known characteristics, the investigator will have reason to believe that any significant differences at the conclusion of the experiment result from the treatment variables. A less desirable method of selecting subjects is to divide one class into two groups. Practice situations in this case are unlike those of actual classes, in which all students receive the same practice schedules.

In classroom research it is both possible and desirable to conduct an experiment without letting students know they are subjects. This increases the external validity of the study because the students will respond as they would in a normal class situation. Subjects who are aware of the investigation are often intrigued by the situation, and may be motivated to perform well or to compete with the other group; their scores, therefore, may not reflect values and influences which would otherwise exist.

the dependent variable

The dependent variable is the measurement of performance. Generally, the test is an established number of scored trials of the motor skill which has been practiced during the learning period. Administration of the test should be the same for all subjects in both groups. The same method, scores, equipment, and facility should be used. In this way, differences in scores between groups will reflect differences in treatment variables rather than differences in test administration. Performance on the dependent variable is statistically analyzed to determine whether there is a significant difference between mean scores. In the example used in this chapter, the mental imagery group and the physical practice group were given a pre-test and a post-test each consisting of twenty trials on the basketball free throw. The score for each subject was the number of baskets made. Performance on the four following dependent variables was analyzed:

1. Pre-test: Did the two groups differ significantly on the pre-test?
2. Post-test: Did the two groups differ significantly on the post-test?
3. Improvement-mental practice group: Did the mental practice group improve significantly from the pre-test to the post-test?

   4. Improvement-physical practice group: Did the physical practice
      group improve significantly from the pre-test to the post-test?

the independent variables

   The independent variables are the treatment variables. They are
the conditions which are being studied. The treatment variables must
be carefully designed and administered so that their application is the
same for all subjects. In the mental practice study, five minutes of
mental practice is one treatment variable and five minutes of physical
practice is a second treatment variable. Instructions for each type
of practice should be standardized for all subjects in the group. The
practice situation should also be the same for all subjects in each
group. For example, in the physical practice group the method of
retrieving balls must be carefully controlled so that it does not interfere with the amount of practice. It is helpful to try out the method of
administering the treatment variables before beginning the investigation. In this way problems are solved which might otherwise affect
the practice situation.

analysis of the data

   The data collected on the dependent variable should be statistically analyzed. Most motor learning research is designed to determine whether there is a significant difference, attributable to the
treatment variables, between groups. In two-group studies, the statistical tool usually applied to determine whether differences between
means are significant is Fisher's t test for uncorrelated means. This
tool is applicable because the two groups of subjects are independent
and the scores will be unrelated or uncorrelated. The investigator may
also be interested in determining whether each group's performance
improved significantly following practice. Because two scores, a pre-
test score and a post-test score, are needed for each subject, they are
related or correlated. Fisher's t test for correlated means is the statistical tool employed. There are many other statistical tools which may
be used; however, the Fisher t tests have been selected for inclusion
in this book since they are applicable for two-group studies conducted
in the classroom situation. The appendix contains an analysis of hy-

pothetical data from the mental practice study used as an example, and in this way the mechanics of statistical analysis are presented.

findings

The results of the statistical analysis are called findings. They are reported as verbal descriptions of what was found. In the study used as an example in this chapter, the following statements represent the findings:

1. There were no significant differences between groups on the pre-test and the post-test.
2. The physical practice group improved significantly from the pre-test to the post-test.
3. The mental practice group showed no improvement from the pre-test to the post-test.

the conclusion

A conclusion is a generalization drawn from the findings of a study. The generalization can be applied under future conditions like those in the study. It is difficult to draw a conclusion based on this mental practice study because though the physical practice group improved significantly, there was no significant difference between groups. The following statement seems justifiable. Under the conditions present in this study, it appears that physical practice hastens the initial learning of the basketball free throw.

PRINCIPLES OF CONDUCTING RESEARCH

To summarize the procedures used in classroom research, the following principles are presented:

1. The purpose of the study should be clearly stated.
2. The study should be limited to a specific age, sex, and skill level.

3. The subjects should be alike in terms of known characteristics.
4. The treatment variables should be standardized.
5. The dependent variable should be a test of the skill used in the study.
6. Performance on the dependent variable should be statistically analyzed.
7. The findings should be based on the results of the statistical analysis.
8. The conclusions should be a generalization drawn from the findings.

Through classroom research you may find the teaching methods most suitable for your particular situation; moreover, your findings may provide the stimulus for future investigation, and you may contribute to the body of man's knowledge. Finally, the constant challenge of classroom research can help teaching remain interesting and exciting throughout your professional career.

BIBLIOGRAPHY

Bell, V. L. 1966. Augmented knowledge of results related to constant and variable errors and its effect upon acquisition and retention of a gross motor skill. Unpublished Ph.D. thesis, University of Southern California.

Broer, M. R. 1955. Evaluation of a basic skills curriculum for women students of low motor ability at the University of Washington. *Research Quarterly* 26:15.

————. 1958. Effectiveness of a general basic skills curriculum for junior high school girls. *Research Quarterly* 29:379.

Brown, Howard, and Messersmith, Lloyd. 1948. An experiment in teaching tumbling with and without motion pictures. *Research Quarterly* 19:304.

Chui, Edward F. 1965. A study of golf-o-tron utilization as a teaching aid in relation to improvement and transfer. *Research Quarterly* 36:147.

Clarke, L. Verdelle. 1960. Effect of mental practice on the development of a certain motor skill. *Research Quarterly* 31:560.

Feinberg, Ruth. 1951. The sound filmstrip as a teaching aid in learning badminton. Unpublished Master's thesis, University of Southern California.

Garland, I. L. 1960. Effectiveness of problem solving method in learning swimming. Unpublished Master's thesis, University of California at Los Angeles.

Gray, C. A., and Brumbach, W. B. 1967. Effect of daylight projection of loop films on learning badminton. *Research Quarterly* 38:562.

Harby, S. F. 1952. *Comparison of mental practice and physical practice in the learning of physical skills.* (SDC 269-7-27) Special Devices Center, Office of Naval Research.

Johnson, Joan. 1961. The effect of knowledge of results on the learning of tennis. Unpublished research project, University of Southern California.

Jones, John G. 1965. Motor learning without demonstration of physical practice, under two conditions of mental practice. *Research Quarterly* 36:270.

Kelly, Darlene A. 1965. The relative effectiveness of selected mental practice techniques in high school girls' acquisition of a gross motor skill. Unpublished Master's thesis, University of Washington.

Kimball, Edwin R. 1934. A comparative study of the whole and part methods of teaching basketball fundamentals. Unpublished Master's thesis, University of Southern California.

Lockhart, Aileene. 1944. The value of motion pictures as an instrumental device in learning a motor skill. *Research Quarterly* 15:181.

Londeree, Ben R. 1967. Effect of training with motion pictures versus flash cards upon football play recognition. *Research Quarterly* 38:202.

Malina, Robert. 1963. Performance changes in a speed-accuracy task as a function of practice under different conditions of information feedback. Unpublished Ph.D. thesis, University of Wisconsin.

Mikesell, Deloris. 1962. The effect of mechanical principle centered instruction on the acquisition of badminton skill. Unpublished Master's thesis, University of Illinois.

Mohr, D. R., and Barrett, M. E. 1962. Effect of knowledge of mechanical principles in learning to perform intermediate swimming skills. *Research Quarterly* 33:574.

Nelson, Dale O. 1958. Effect of slow motion loop films on the learning of golf. *Research Quarterly* 29:37.

Niemeyer. R. K. 1958. Part versus whole methods and massed versus distributed practice in learning of selected large muscle activities. Unpublished Ph.D. thesis, University of Southern California.

Plese, Elliot R. 1968. Comparison of videotape replay with a traditional approach in the teaching of selected gymnastic skills. *Abstracts of Research Papers: AAHPER 1968 Convention.* Washington, D.C.: American Association for Health, Physical Education, and Recreation.

Purdy, Bonnie J., and Stallard, Mary L. 1967. Effect of two learning methods and two grips on acquisition of power and accuracy in the golf swing of college women. *Research Quarterly* 38:480.

Singer, Robert N. 1966. Transfer effects and ultimate success in archery due to degree of difficulty of the initial learning. *Research Quarterly* 37:532.

Surburg. Paul R. 1968. Audio, visual, and audio-visual instruction with mental practice in developing the forehand tennis drive. *Research Quarterly* 39:728.

Watkins, David L. 1963. Motion pictures as an aid in correcting baseball batting faults. *Research Quarterly* 34:228–33.

Wickstrom, Ralph L. 1958. Comparative study of methodologies for teaching gymnastics and tumbling stunts. *Research Quarterly* 29:10.

Wills, Keith C. 1965. The effect of mental practice and physical practice on learning a motor skill. Unpublished Master's thesis, Arkansas State College.

Woods, John B. 1967. The effect of varied instructional emphasis upon the development of a motor skill. *Research Quarterly* 38:132.

Young, Olive. 1954. Rate of learning in relation to spacing of practice periods in archery and badminton. *Research Quarterly* 25:231.

Appendix

t tests for uncorrelated means

One of the questions asked in the mental practice study was, "Did the two groups differ significantly on the pre-test?" We hope they did not differ; the two groups should be alike at the beginning of the experiment so that any differences at the end can be attributed to the treatment variable. In this case, each person was tested on twenty trials of the basketball free throw before the treatment variable was introduced. The scores of the subjects in the two groups are presented in Table 2. They are listed under the heading "X," which is the symbol for "raw score." The mean or average for each group is determined by adding the raw scores and dividing by the number of subjects in the group. The symbol for the "sum of raw scores" is "ΣX," and the symbol for the number of subjects is "N." Therefore, the equation used to determine the mean ("M") is

$$M = \frac{\Sigma X}{N}.$$

The mean difference ("M_{diff}") is determined by subtracting one mean from the other. A subscript number 1 or 2 designates which group is being talked about. For example, M_1 stands for the mean of group 1, the physical practice group.

We must now ask whether a mean difference of .37 is significant or due to chance. To answer this question, we test our difference against the hypothesis that there is no difference between the means. This hypothesis is called the null hypothesis. Symbolically it can be written H_o $M_1 = M_2$. Verbally, the null hypothesis (H_o) states that the mean of one group equals the mean of the second group. The test of our mean difference is Fisher's $\underline{t}$ for uncorrelated means. The formula for $\underline{t}$ is:

$$\underline{t} = \frac{M_{diff}}{SD_{M_{diff}}}$$

SD is the symbol for standard error and the subscript $_{M_{diff}}$ further defines the symbol as the standard error of the difference between means.

TABLE 2
Pre-test Raw Scores, Means, and Mean Difference

Group 1 (Physical Practice)		Group 2 (Mental Practice)	
S	X	S	X
1	0	1	0
2	1	2	0
3	1	3	0
4	4	4	3
5	3	5	0
6	3	6	6
7	1	7	0
8	0	8	5
9	4	9	4
10	3	10	3
11	0	11	0
12	0	12	1
13	1	13	2
14	0	14	3
15	1		
16	3		
$\Sigma = 25$		$\Sigma = 27$	

$$M_1 = \frac{\Sigma X_1}{N_1} = \frac{25}{16} = 1.56 \qquad M_2 = \frac{\Sigma X_2}{N_2} = \frac{27}{14} = 1.93$$

$$M_{diff} = 1.93 - 1.56 = .37$$

Verbally, $\underline{t}$ equals the mean difference divided by the standard error of the mean difference. In order to use this formula, we must find the $SD_{M_{\text{diff}}}$, or the standard error of the mean difference. The following formula is used:

$$SD_{M_{\text{diff}}} = \sqrt{\frac{\Sigma x_1^2 + \Sigma x_2^2}{N_1 + N_2 - 2} \left(\frac{1}{N_1} + \frac{1}{N_2}\right)},$$

where Σx^2 is the sum of squares.

Before we can find the $SD_{M_{\text{diff}}}$, we must find Σx^2 for each group. The symbol Σx^2 means sum of squares; it is found by subtracting the squared sum of the raw scores divided by the number of scores from the sum of the squared scores. That is,

$$\Sigma x^2 = \Sigma(X^2) - \frac{(\Sigma X)^2}{N}.$$

We found ΣX in calculating the mean. Since X stands for raw score, the symbol ΣX^2 tells us that we must square each score and then sum the squares. These figures are then plugged into the formula for Σx^2 (see Table 3).

We are now ready to find $SD_{M_{\text{diff}}}$, using the following formula:

$$SD_{M_{\text{diff}}} = \sqrt{\frac{\Sigma x_1^2 + \Sigma x_2^2}{N_1 + N_2 - 2} \left(\frac{1}{N_1} + \frac{1}{N_2}\right)}$$

$$= \sqrt{\frac{34.94 + 56.93}{16 + 14 - 2} \left(\frac{1}{16} + \frac{1}{14}\right)}$$

$$= \sqrt{\frac{91.87}{28} (.134)}$$

$$= \sqrt{(3.29)(.134)} = \sqrt{.44} = .66$$

Knowing the $SD_{M_{\text{diff}}}$, we can solve for $\underline{t}$, using the following formula:

$$\underline{t} = \frac{M_{\text{diff}}}{SD_{M_{\text{diff}}}}$$

Plugging in the figures from the experiment, we get

$$\underline{t} = \frac{.37}{.66} = .56$$

TABLE 3
Sum of Squares, Pre-test Scores

Group 1 (Physical Practice)				Group 2 (Mental Practice)	
S	X	X^2		X	X^2
1	0	0		0	0
2	1	1		0	0
3	1	1		0	0
4	4	16		3	9
5	3	9		0	0
6	3	9		6	36
7	1	1		0	0
8	0	0		5	25
9	4	16		4	16
10	3	9		3	9
11	0	0		0	0
12	0	0		1	1
13	1	1		2	4
14	0	0		3	9
15	1	1			
16	3	9			
	$\Sigma = 27$	109		$\Sigma = 25$	73

$$M_1 = 1.56 \qquad\qquad M_2 = 1.93$$

$$M_{\text{diff}} = \begin{array}{c} 1.93 \\ -1.56 \\ \hline .37 \end{array}$$

$$\Sigma x_1^2 = \Sigma X^2 - \frac{(\Sigma X)^2}{N} \qquad\qquad \Sigma x_2^2 = \Sigma X^2 - \frac{(\Sigma X)^2}{N}$$

$$= 73 - \frac{25^2}{16} \qquad\qquad\qquad = 109 - \frac{27^2}{14}$$

$$= 73 - \frac{625}{16} \qquad\qquad\qquad = 109 - \frac{729}{14}$$

$$= 73 - 39.06 \qquad\qquad\qquad = 109 - 52.07$$

$$= 34.94 \qquad\qquad\qquad\qquad = 56.93$$

It is necessary to use a table to determine whether the value of $\underline{t}$ is significant. In order to use the table we must find the degrees of freedom (df). The following formula is used:

$$df = N_1 + N_2 - 2$$

TABLE 4

Table of t, for use in determining the significance of statistics at the .05 level of confidence. A value equal to or greater than that shown in the table means that the mean difference is significant at the .05 level of confidence.

df	t	df	t	df	t
1	12.71	15	2.13	29	2.04
2	4.30	16	2.12	30	2.04
3	3.18	17	2.11	35	2.03
4	2.78	18	2.10	40	2.02
5	2.57	19	2.09	45	2.02
6	2.45	20	2.09	50	2.01
7	2.36	21	2.08	60	2.00
8	2.31	22	2.07	70	2.00
9	2.26	23	2.07	80	1.99
10	2.23	24	2.06	90	1.99
11	2.20	25	2.06	100	1.98
12	2.18	26	2.06	125	1.98
13	2.16	27	2.05	150	1.98
14	2.14	28	2.05	∞	1.96

Note: Reproduced with permission of the publisher from Henry Garrett, *Statistics in Psychology and Education* (New York: David McKay Company, Inc., 1958).

The degrees of freedom are the number of scores which vary around a parameter. For example, if there are 16 scores for which the mean is known, the deviations of these scores from the mean will equal zero; 15 of these scores may vary, but the sixteenth score is fixed. For this reason, one degree of freedom is lost for each distribution of scores. Because we have two distributions of scores we lose two degrees of freedom. In our problem, df = 16 + 14 − 2 = 28. Looking at Table 4, we see a column headed "df." Moving down to 28 degrees of freedom, we look across and see the value 2.05. If our value for t were greater than the value in the table, we would have a significant difference between our means at the .05 level of confidence; which means that in rejecting the null hypothesis we would probably be wrong only five times out of one hundred.

However, our value for t is less than the value in the table of t; therefore, we accept the null hypothesis that there is no difference between the means.

TABLE 5
Analysis of Post-test Mean Difference

	Group 1 (Physical Practice)			Group 2 (Mental Practice)	
S	X	X^2		X	X^2
1	0	0		1	1
2	0	0		2	4
3	5	25		1	1
4	6	36		0	0
5	7	49		5	25
6	1	1		2	4
7	2	4		1	1
8	4	16		2	4
9	3	9		2	4
10	5	25		1	1
11	4	16		3	9
12	7	49		10	100
13	1	1		4	16
14	2	4		6	36
15	9	81			
16	11	121			
	$\Sigma = 67$	437		$\Sigma = 40$	206

$$M_1 = 4.18 \qquad\qquad M_2 = 2.86$$

$$M_{diff} = 4.18 - 2.86 = 1.32$$

$$\Sigma x_1^2 = \Sigma(X^2) - \frac{(\Sigma X)^2}{N} \qquad \Sigma x_2^2 = \Sigma(X^2) - \frac{(\Sigma X)^2}{N}$$

$$= 437 - \frac{67^2}{16} \qquad\qquad = 206 - \frac{40^2}{14}$$

$$= 437 - \frac{4489}{16} \qquad\qquad = 206 - \frac{1600}{14}$$

$$= 437 - 280.56 \qquad\qquad = 206 - 114.29$$

$$= 156.44 \qquad\qquad\qquad = 91.71$$

$$SD_{M_{diff}} = \sqrt{\frac{\Sigma x_1^2 + \Sigma x_1^2}{N_1 + N_2 - 2}\left(\frac{1}{N_1} + \frac{1}{N_2}\right)}$$

$$= \sqrt{\frac{156.44 + 91.71}{16 + 14 - 2}\left(\frac{1}{16} + \frac{1}{14}\right)}$$

$$= \sqrt{.97} = .98$$

$$t = \frac{M_{diff}}{SD_{M_{diff}}} = \frac{1.32}{.98} = 1.35$$

$$df = N_1 + N_2 - 2$$
$$= 16 + 14 - 2 = 28$$

The post-test served as a dependent variable in our study. If the post-test means differed significantly, we would conclude that the treatment variable producing the highest mean represented the best method of practice. Again we will use Fisher's t for uncorrelated means to determine whether our obtained mean difference is significant. The statistical analysis is presented in Table 5. The obtained value of t is 1.35. With 28 degrees of freedom, a value of 2.05 is needed for significance. Therefore, we accept the null hypothesis that there is no difference between the means.

t for correlated means

In the mental practice study we wish to determine whether the groups showed any significant improvement following the practice schedule. We have a pre-test score and a post-test score for each subject. The score we are interested in for our analysis is the difference between the test scores; this difference is labeled "X" for raw score. Table 6 represents the pre-test and post-test scores for group 1,

TABLE 6
Raw Scores, Means, and Mean Difference of Physical Practice Group

S	Pre-test	Post-test	X
1	0	0	0
2	1	0	−1
3	1	5	4
4	4	6	2
5	3	7	4
6	3	1	−2
7	1	2	1
8	0	4	4
9	4	3	−1
10	3	5	2
11	0	4	4
12	0	7	7
13	1	1	0
14	0	2	2
15	1	9	8
16	3	11	8
Σ	25	67	42
M	1.56	4.19	2.63

$$M_{\text{diff}} = 4.19 - 1.56$$
$$= 2.63$$

the physical practice group. The means for each test and the mean difference (mean of the difference) are also shown. The mean difference represents the group's improvement.

The group showed an improvement of 2.63 free throws following physical practice. We must now ask ourselves whether this mean difference is significant. Again the difference is tested against the null hypothesis that there is no difference between means. We test our mean difference using Fisher's t for correlated means. The formula for t is:

$$t = \frac{M_{diff}}{SD_{M_{diff}}}$$

However, the formula for $SD_{M_{diff}}$ differs from the formula used for uncorrelated means. It is:

$$SD_{M_{diff}} = \sqrt{\frac{\Sigma x^2}{N(N-1)}}$$

Before we can find the $SD_{M_{diff}}$, we must find Σx^2. The formula for the sum of squares is the same formula we used before, with X representing the difference in scores for each subject. The formula for Σx^2 is:

$$\Sigma x^2 = \Sigma(X^2) - \frac{(\Sigma X)^2}{N}$$

Again we square the raw score X for each subject and plug the figures into the formula (see Table 7). The sum of squares equals 149.75.

We are now ready to find $SD_{M_{diff}}$ using the following formula:

$$SD_{M_{diff}} = \sqrt{\frac{\Sigma x^2}{N(N-1)}}$$

$$= \sqrt{\frac{149.75}{240}}$$

$$= \sqrt{.624} = .79$$

Knowing the $SD_{M_{diff}}$, we can solve for $\underline{t}$.

$$\underline{t} = \frac{M_{diff}}{SD_{M_{diff}}}$$

$$= \frac{2.63}{.79}$$

$$= 3.33$$

TABLE 7
Sum of Squares for Physical Practice Group

S	Pre-test	Post-test	X	X^2
1	0	0	0	0
2	1	0	—1	1
3	1	5	4	16
4	4	6	2	4
5	3	7	4	16
6	3	1	—2	4
7	1	2	1	1
8	0	4	4	16
9	4	3	—1	1
10	3	5	2	4
11	0	4	4	16
12	0	7	7	49
13	1	1	0	0
14	0	2	2	4
15	1	9	8	64
16	3	11	8	64
Σ	25	67	42	260

$$\Sigma x^2 = \Sigma(X^2) - \frac{(\Sigma X)^2}{N}$$

$$= 260 - \frac{42^2}{16}$$

$$= 260 - \frac{1764}{16}$$

$$= 149.75$$

To determine whether the value of $\underline{t}$ is significant, we use the table of degrees of freedom. The following formula is used:

$$df = N - 1$$

In our problem, $df = N - 1 = 16 - 1 = 15$. Looking at Table 4 under df, we find 15. Moving across, we see the value 2.13. Our value for t (3.33) is greater than that shown in the table. Therefore, we know that we have a significant difference between means at the .05 level of confidence, and we reject the null hypothesis that there is no difference between the means.

The same statistical analysis is conducted to determine whether the mental practice group improved significantly. This analysis is presented in Table 8. The value of t is .98 with 13 degrees of freedom. The value of 2.16 must be exceeded for significance. Therefore, we accept the null hypothesis that there is no difference between means.

TABLE 8

Analysis of Improvement for the Mental Practice Group

S	Pre-test	Post-test	X	X²
1	0	1	1	1
2	0	2	2	4
3	0	1	1	1
4	3	0	—3	9
5	0	5	5	25
6	6	2	—4	16
7	0	1	1	1
8	5	2	—3	9
9	4	2	—2	4
10	3	1	—2	4
11	0	3	3	9
12	1	10	9	81
13	2	4	2	4
14	3	6	3	9
$\Sigma =$ 27	40	13	177	

$$M = 1.93 \qquad 2.86 \qquad .93$$

$$M_{diff} = 2.86 - 1.93 = .93$$

$$\Sigma x^2 = \Sigma(X^2) - \frac{(\Sigma X)^2}{N}$$

$$= 177 - \frac{13^2}{14}$$

$$= 177 - \frac{169}{14}$$

$$= 177 - 12.07 = 164.93$$

$$SD_{M_{diff}} = \sqrt{\frac{\Sigma x^2}{N(N-1)}}$$

$$= \sqrt{\frac{164.93}{14(14-1)}}$$

$$= \sqrt{\frac{164.93}{182}}$$

$$= \sqrt{.91} = .95$$

$$\underline{t} = \frac{M_{diff}}{SD_{M_{diff}}} = \frac{.93}{.95} = .98$$

$$\mathbf{df} = N - 1$$
$$= 14 - 1 = 13$$

BIBLIOGRAPHY

Garrett, Henry E. 1965. *Statistics in psychology and education.* 5th ed. New York: Longmans, Green.

Runyon, Richard P., and Haber, Audrey. 1967. *Fundamentals of behavioral statistics.* Reading, Massachusetts: Addison-Wesley.

Siegal, S. 1956. *Non-parametric statistics.* New York: McGraw-Hill.

Subject Index

Author Index